McDougal Littell

WORLD HISTORY

PATTERNS OF INTERACTION

In-Depth Resources: Unit 1

Beginnings of Civilization

McDougal Littell
A DIVISION OF HOUGHTON MIFFLIN COMPANY

Acknowledgments

CHAPTER 1

Excerpt from *Lucy: The Beginning of Humankind* by Donald C. Johanson and Maitland A. Edey. Copyright © 1981 by Donald C. Johanson and Maitland A. Edey. Reprinted with the permission of Simon & Schuster, Inc.

Excerpt from "Window on the Stone Age" by Leon Jaroff, *Time Magazine*, January 30, 1995. Copyright © 1995 by Time Inc. Reprinted by permission.

Excerpt from *The Clan of the Cave Bear* by Jean M. Auel. Copyright © 1980 by Jean M. Auel. Reprinted by permission of Crown Publishers, Inc.

CHAPTER 2

Excerpt from *Letters from Mesopotamia*, translated by A. Leo Oppenheim. Copyright © 1967 by The University of Chicago. All rights reserved. Reprinted by permission of The University of Chicago Press.

Excerpt from *The Ancient Near East, Volume 1*, edited by James B. Pritchard. Copyright © 1958, 1986 by Princeton University Press. Reprinted by permission of Princeton University Press.

CHAPTER 3

"To Dawn," and "To Night," from *The Rig Veda*, translated by Nicol Macnicol. Reprinted by permission of Everyman's Library, David Campbell Publishers, Ltd.

From *Bhagavad-Gita* by Barbara Stoler Miller. Translation copyright © 1986 by Barbara Stoler Miller. Used by permission of Bantam Books, a division of Bantam Doubleday Dell Publishing Group, Inc.

Excerpt from *Ramayana: King Rama's Way*, translated by William Buck. Copyright © 1976 by The Regents of the University of California. Reprinted by permission of the University of California Press.

Excerpt from *Siddhartha* by Herman Hesse. Copyright © 1951 by New Directions Publishing Corp. Reprinted by permission of New Directions Publishing Corp.

CHAPTER 4

Excerpt from "Assyrian Capture of Jerusalem," from *Ancient Near East Texts, Second Edition*, edited by James B. Pritchard. Copyright © 1969 by Princeton University Press. Reprinted by permission of Princeton University Press.

Excerpt from *Intrigues: Studies of the Chan Kuo Ts'e* by James Crump (Ann Arbor: The University of Michigan Press, 1964). Reprinted by permission of The University of Michigan Press.

Excerpt from *The Analects of Confucius*, translated by Arthur Waley. Reprinted by permission of HarperCollins Publishers Ltd.

ISBN-13: 978-0-618-40911-2   ISBN-10: 0-618-40911-4

Printed in the United States of America.

9 - 0928 - 09

To the Teacher v

Strategies for Reading Your History Book viii

Unit 1 Beginnings of Civilization 4 Million B.C.–200 B.C.

CHAPTER 1 The Peopling of the World, Prehistory–2500 B.C.

GUIDED READING
Section 1 1
Section 2 2
Section 3 3

BUILDING VOCABULARY 4

SKILLBUILDER PRACTICE: Interpreting Maps 5

GEOGRAPHY APPLICATION: Çatal Hüyük 6

PRIMARY SOURCES
from *Lucy: The Beginnings of Humankind* by Donald Johanson 8
Lascaux Cave Painting 10
from "Window on the Stone Age" by Leon Jaroff 11

LITERATURE SELECTION
from *The Clan of the Cave Bear* by Jean M. Auel 12

HISTORY MAKERS
Mary Leakey 15
The Iceman 16

CONNECTIONS ACROSS TIME AND CULTURES
From Ancient to Modern Communities 17

RETEACHING ACTIVITIES
Section 1 18
Section 2 19
Section 3 20

CHAPTER 2 Early River Valley Civilizations, 3500 B.C.–450 B.C.

GUIDED READING
Section 1 21
Section 2 22
Section 3 23
Section 4 24

BUILDING VOCABULARY 25

SKILLBUILDER PRACTICE: Interpreting Visual Sources 26

GEOGRAPHY APPLICATION: Egypt and the Nile Delta 27

PRIMARY SOURCES
Assyrian Letters 29
from *The Code of Hammurabi* 30
Sphinx of Amenemhet III 32

LITERATURE SELECTIONS
Ancient Proverbs 33
from *The Epic of Gilgamesh* 34

HISTORY MAKERS

Hammurabi 36

Tutankhamen 37

CONNECTIONS ACROSS TIME AND CULTURES

River Civilizations in the Ancient World 38

SCIENCE & TECHNOLOGY

Early Water Engineering 39

RETEACHING ACTIVITIES

Section 1 40

Section 2 41

Section 3 42

Section 4 43

CHAPTER 3 People and Ideas on the Move, 2000 B.C.–250 B.C.

GUIDED READING

Section 1 44

Section 2 45

Section 3 46

Section 4 47

BUILDING VOCABULARY 48

SKILLBUILDER PRACTICE: Forming Opinions 49

GEOGRAPHY APPLICATION: Early Eastern Mediterranean Civilizations . . 50

PRIMARY SOURCES

from the *Rig Veda* 52

from the *Bhagavad-Gita* 53

Dolphin Fresco from Knossos 54

The Ten Commandments 55

LITERATURE SELECTIONS

from the *Ramayana* by Valmiki 56

from *Siddhartha* by Herman Hesse 57

HISTORY MAKERS

Siddhartha Gautama 59

Herodotus 60

CONNECTIONS ACROSS TIME AND CULTURES

Religions in the Ancient World 61

RETEACHING ACTIVITIES

Section 1 62

Section 2 63

Section 3 64

Section 4 65

CHAPTER 4 First Age of Empires, 1570 B.C.–200 B.C.

GUIDED READING

Section 1 66

Section 2 67

Section 3 68

Section 4 69

BUILDING VOCABULARY 70

SKILLBUILDER PRACTICE: Recognizing Effects 71

GEOGRAPHY APPLICATION: Babylon 72

PRIMARY SOURCES
    from Assyrian Capture of Jerusalem by Sennacherib 74
    "To the Fire" from the *Zend-Avesta* 75
    from *Intrigues of the Warring States* 76
    from the *Analects* by Confucius 77

LITERATURE SELECTIONS
    "Ozymandias" by Percy Bysshe Shelley 78
    "The Destruction of Sennacherib" by George Gordon, Lord Byron 79
    "Babylon" by Alfred, Lord Tennyson 80

HISTORY MAKERS
    Hatshepsut 81
    Sennacherib 82

CONNECTIONS ACROSS TIME AND CULTURES
    Empires of Southwest Asia 83

RETEACHING ACTIVITIES
    Section 1 84
    Section 2 85
    Section 3 86
    Section 4 87

ANSWER KEY 88

To the Teacher

The materials in the *In-Depth Resources* books have been carefully chosen to support and enhance the instruction given in each unit of *World History: Patterns of Interaction*. Whether you are looking for help with skill practice and reteaching or for varied enrichment opportunities, you will find the resources to target the individual needs of your students.

There are eight *In-Depth Resources* books, one for each unit of the textbook. The resources for each unit are divided by chapter and correspond to specific sections within each chapter. The Planning Guide, located in the Teacher's Edition at the beginning of each chapter, can help you plan ahead and integrate these ancillary resources into your regular instruction.

What follows is a brief description of the components of each *In-Depth Resources* book.

GUIDED READING

Each one-page Guided Reading worksheet is designed to help students access the information in a particular section of a chapter. Oriented primarily toward reading skills, the worksheets help students focus on essential aspects of the chapter sections by developing their note-taking skills. As they take notes, students learn to summarize main ideas, identify causes and effects, compare and contrast, and trace chronological sequences of events. Graphic organizers, such as charts and time lines, help to demonstrate these historical relationships on a visual level. In addition, each Guided Reading worksheet helps students to identify the key terms and names in the chapter section they are studying.

BUILDING VOCABULARY

Use these one-page worksheets to help students strengthen their knowledge of the significant terms and people of each chapter. The worksheets provide a variety of high-interest activities that challenge students' recall and reinforce key terms and names. Each worksheet also includes an exercise to help students practice their writing skills.

SKILLBUILDER PRACTICE

These one-page worksheets give students practice in applying the specific social studies skills taught in the Skillbuilder Handbook at the back of *World History: Patterns of Interaction*. In general, each worksheet features a reading passage containing in-depth information on a topic treated in the corresponding chapter. The reading is followed by an activity that requires students to apply a specific thinking skill needed for understanding history. Use these worksheets for reinforcement or for reteaching.

GEOGRAPHY APPLICATION

Use these worksheets to reinforce geography skills and to provide students with practice in the skills. Each two-page worksheet includes the following parts:

- a reading passage that deals with a topic from the corresponding chapter
- a related graphic (map, chart, or graph) for students to interpret
- a page of questions about the passage and the graphic

The majority of the graphics on the worksheets are maps—some of them accompanied by charts or graphs containing additional information. These complex and graphically sophisticated worksheets are labeled according to the five geographic themes: location, place, movement, region, and human–environment interaction.

PRIMARY SOURCES

Because primary sources both enrich and enliven the study of history, they are invaluable in any classroom. The primary sources collected for each chapter were chosen to stimulate as well as inform. Included are items that add dimension to the relevant historical period—such as photographs of artifacts, personal letters, diary entries, and eyewitness accounts of significant events—as well as important historical documents. The impact of these documents and illustrations is enhanced by activities that invite students to participate in history through discussion, research, and short projects.

The primary sources in the *In-Depth Resources* books are one- or two-page selections intended for use in short time periods or as homework. For longer selections, see the *Electronic Library of Primary Sources* available on CD-ROM. The *Teacher's Resource Book* for the *Patterns of Interaction* video series also includes primary sources and extension activities.

LITERATURE SELECTIONS
Literature from other cultures—for example, *The Odyssey*, *The Epic of Gilgamesh*, and *The Tale of Genji*—can give students glimpses of the vitality and imagination of peoples with lives quite different from theirs. Literature set in historical periods—for example, *The Clan of the Cave Bear*, *Julius Caesar*, and *A Tale of Two Cities*—can help them imagine life in other times. The literature selections in the *In-Depth Resources* books have been chosen with the goal of presenting a balance of literature produced in other cultures and literature offering imaginative insights into other cultures. Many excerpts are long enough to provide students with sustained imaginative experiences. Use the selections as imaginative gateways into history.

HISTORYMAKERS
These biographical sketches of the prominent and the not-so-prominent are provided to bring a human dimension to the vast array of historical figures presented in *World History: Patterns of Interaction*. There are two one-page biographies for each chapter.

CONNECTIONS ACROSS TIME AND CULTURES
World History: Patterns of Interaction is designed to encourage teachers and students to make connections across time and cultures—to find characteristics shared by many generations and many peoples. These worksheets will help students appreciate the "big picture" of world history and deepen their understanding of similarities and differences among various cultures. There is one worksheet for each chapter.

SCIENCE & TECHNOLOGY
These brief articles will help students explore a variety of topics in science and technology. Each article takes the idea in one of the textbook's ten Science & Technology features and extends it into a related field of the same time period. Use these articles as homework or as extension activities.

RETEACHING ACTIVITIES
These on-page review worksheets help students to better comprehend the main ideas of the textbook. Corresponding with each section of the book, these worksheets offer students a variety of challenging review activities that focus on the key ideas, people, and events of the history they read. Use these pages as a section quiz or as in-class activities to reinforce the main points of a chapter.

As a study aid for students whose first language is Spanish, the following worksheets from the *In-Depth Resources* books have been translated and can be found in the book titled *In-Depth Resources in Spanish*.
- Guided Reading
- Skillbuilder Practice
- Geography Application

Strategies for Reading Your History Book

History is filled with facts and dates, personalities and actions, and monumental events—a wealth of details that can excite, inform, and occasionally overwhelm a reader. The most important strategy to remember as you read a history textbook is to tune out the details and form the "big picture" of history first. Once you give yourself a chance to "engage" with the text—to find events or people that trigger your curiosity—the details will make more sense. Use the strategies shown here to help you approach your reading.

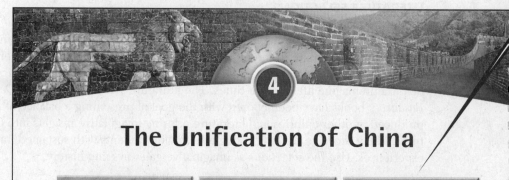

4

The Unification of China

MAIN IDEA	WHY IT MATTERS NOW	TERMS & NAMES
RELIGIOUS AND ETHICAL SYSTEMS The social disorder of the warring states contributed to the development of three Chinese ethical systems.	The people, events, and ideas that shaped China's early history continue to influence China's role in today's world.	• Confucius • *I Ching* • filial piety • yin and yang • bureaucracy • Qin Dynasty • Daoism • Shi Huangdi • Legalism • autocracy

SETTING THE STAGE The Zhou Dynasty, as you read in Chapter 2, lasted for at least eight centuries, from approximately 1027 to 256 B.C. For the first 300 years of their long reign, the Zhou kings controlled a large empire, including both eastern and western lands. Local rulers reported to the king, who had the ultimate power. By the latter years of the Zhou Dynasty, the lords of dependent territories began to think of themselves as independent kings. Their almost constant conflict, which is known as "the warring states period," led to the decline of the Zhou Dynasty.

Confucius and the Social Order

Toward the end of the Zhou Dynasty, China moved away from its ancient values of social order, harmony, and respect for authority. Chinese scholars and philosophers developed different solutions to restore these values.

Confucius Urges Harmony China's most influential scholar was **Confucius** (kuhn•FYOO•shuhs). Born in 551 B.C., Confucius lived in a time when the Zhou Dynasty was in decline. He led a scholarly life, studying and teaching history, music, and moral character.

Confucius was born at a time of crisis and violence in China. He had a deep desire to restore the order and moral living of earlier times to his society. Confucius believed that social order, harmony, and good government could be restored in China if society were organized around five basic relationships. These were the relationships between: 1) ruler and subject, 2) father and son, 3) husband and wife, 4) older brother and younger brother, and 5) friend and friend. A code of proper conduct regulated each of these relationships. For example, rulers should practice kindness and virtuous living. In return, subjects should be loyal and law-abiding.

Three of Confucius's five relationships were based upon the family. Confucius stressed that children should practice **filial piety**, or respect for their parents and ancestors. Filial piety, according to Confucius, meant devoting oneself to one's parents during their lifetime. It also required honoring their memory after death through the performance of certain rituals.

TAKING NOTES
Recognizing Effects
Use a web to indicate how the chaos of the warring states affected the philosophy, politics, and cities of China.

Philosophy

Chaos of the warring states

Politics   Cities

104 Chapter 4

Strategy: Look at the heads and subheads in each section to get a general understanding of the subject.

Try This: Preview the heads for Chapter 1, Section 2, on page 14. What questions do they raise? What do you expect to learn in this section?

Strategy: Use the graphic organizer shown on the first page of each section to enhance your understanding of the content covered. Simple graphics like this one can help you organize information in the section.

Try This: Look at the graphic organizer in Chapter 2, Section 3, on page 23. Summarizing the characteristics of a civilization in list form will help you remember what you read.

Strategy: Look for key terms & names that are defined in context and provide clues to the section's content.

Try This: Locate the terms at the top of page 5. Then look at page 7. Which of these terms appear on that page? How did you recognize them?

Strategy: Use vocabulary notes at point of use to help you with unfamiliar terms.

Try This: Look at page 15. What word is defined in the inner margin?

Strategy: When you've read through the main narrative on page 00, read the side features. Ask yourself how the information in the side features adds to your understanding of the content.

Try This: Look at the History in Depth feature on page 15. How might it help you understand the content under the head, "The Neolithic Revolution"?

In the following passage, Confucius—the "Master"—expresses his thoughts on the concept:

PRIMARY SOURCE

Ziyou [a disciple of Confucius] asked about filial piety. The Master said: "Nowadays people think they are dutiful sons when they feed their parents. Yet they also feed their dogs and horses. Unless there is respect, where is the difference?"

CONFUCIUS, *Analects* 2.7

Vocabulary
legend: a story handed down from earlier times, especially one believed to be historical

Confucius wanted to reform Chinese society by showing rulers how to govern wisely. Impressed by Confucius's wisdom, the duke of Lu appointed him minister of justice. According to legend, Confucius so overwhelmed people by his kindness and courtesy that almost overnight, crime vanished from Lu. When the duke's ways changed, however, Confucius became disillusioned and resigned.

Confucius spent the remainder of his life teaching. His students later collected his words in a book called the *Analects*. A disciple named Mencius (MEHN•shee•uhs) also spread Confucius's ideas.

Confucian Ideas About Government Confucius said that education could transform a humbly born person into a gentleman. In saying this, he laid the groundwork for the creation of a **bureaucracy**, a trained civil service, or those who run the government. According to Confucius, a gentleman had four virtues: "In his private conduct he was courteous, in serving his master he was punctilious [precise], in providing for the needs of the people he gave them even more than their due; in exacting service from the people, he was just." Education became critically important to career advancement in the bureaucracy.

Confucianism was never a religion, but it was an ethical system, a system based on accepted principles of right and wrong. It became the foundation for Chinese government and social order. In addition, the ideas of Confucius spread beyond China and influenced civilizations throughout East Asia.

History Makers

Confucius
551–479 B.C.
Confucius was born to a poor family. As an adult, he earned his living as a teacher. But he longed to put his principles into action by advising political leaders. Finally, at around age 50, Confucius won a post as minister in his home state. According to legend, he set such a virtuous example that a purse lying in the middle of the street would be untouched for days.

After Confucius resigned his post as minister, he returned to teaching. He considered himself a failure because he had never held high office. Yet Confucius's ideas have molded Chinese thought for centuries.

Laozi
sixth century B.C.
Although a person named Laozi is credited with being the first philosopher of Daoism, no one knows for sure whether he really existed. Legend has it that Laozi's mother carried him in her womb for 62 years and that he was born with white hair and wrinkled skin. Laozi's followers claimed that he was a contemporary of Confucius.

Unlike Confucius, however, Laozi believed that government should do as little as possible and leave the people alone. Laozi thought that people could do little to influence the outcome of events. Daoism offered communion with nature as an alternative to political chaos.

INTEGRATED TECHNOLOGY

RESEARCH LINKS For more on Confucius and Laozi, go to **classzone.com**

Other Ethical Systems

In addition to Confucius, other Chinese scholars and philosophers developed ethical systems with very different philosophies. Some stressed the importance of nature, others, the power of government.

Daoists Seek Harmony For a Chinese thinker named Laozi (low•dzuh), who may have lived during the sixth century B.C., only the natural order was important. The natural order involves relations among all living things. His book *Dao De Jing* (*The Way of Virtue*) expressed Laozi's belief. He said that a universal force called the Dao (dow), meaning "the Way," guides all things. Of all the creatures of nature,

First Age of Empires **105**

More Strategies for Reading...

Strategy: Use the Main Idea questions to check your understanding of what you read.

Try This: Read the Main Idea questions on page 16. What details from the text can help you answer these questions?

Strategy: Review the maps in each section. Think about how geography affects historical events.

Try This: Look at the large map on page 17. How does it add to your understanding of the emergence of agriculture in the ancient world?

of wood and animal skins. Animal bones found with Neanderthal fossils indicate the ability of Neanderthals to hunt in subarctic regions of Europe. To cut up and skin their prey, they fashioned stone blades, scrapers, and other tools. The Neanderthals survived for some 170,000 years and then mysteriously vanished about 30,000 years ago.

Cro-Magnons Emerge About 40,000 years ago, a group of prehistoric humans called Cro-Magnons appeared. Their skeletal remains show that they are identical to modern humans. The remains also indicate that they were probably strong and generally about five-and-one-half feet tall. Cro-Magnons migrated from North Africa to Europe and Asia.

Cro-Magnons made many new tools with specialized uses. Unlike Neanderthals, they planned their hunts. They studied animals' habits and stalked their prey. Evidently, Cro-Magnons' superior hunting strategies allowed them to survive more easily. This may have caused Cro-Magnon populations to grow at a slightly faster rate and eventually replace the Neanderthals. Cro-Magnons' advanced skill in spoken language may also have helped them to plan more difficult projects. This cooperation perhaps gave them an edge over the Neanderthals.

MAIN IDEA
Comparing
How were Neanderthals similar to people today?

Early Human Migration, 1,600,000–10,000 B.C.
INTERACTIVE

Heidelberg, Germany 600,000 years ago
Mladeč, Czech Rep. 33,000 years ago
Malta, Russia 15,000 years ago
Diuktai Cave, Russia 14,000 years ago
Ubeidiya, Israel 1 million years ago
Lantian, China 700,000 years ago
Gafzeh, Israel 92,000 years ago
Linjiang, China 67,000 years ago
Tighenif, Algeria 700,000 years ago
Blackwater Draw, U.S. 11,000 years ago
Meadowcroft Rockshelter, U.S. 12,000 years ago
Lake Turkana, Kenya 1.6 million years ago
Tabon Cave, Philippines 30,000 years ago
Trinil, Indonesia 700,000 years ago
Pedra Furada, Brazil 12,000–30,000 years ago
Klasies River Mouth, South Africa 100,000 years ago
Lake Mungo, Australia 38,000 years ago
Monte Verde, Chile 12,000–33,000 years ago

- Homo erectus fossil site
- Homo sapiens fossil site
- Homo erectus migration route
- Homo sapiens migration route
- Extent of the last glacier, 18,000 B.C.
- Extent of land areas 18,000 B.C.

2,000 Miles
4,000 Kilometers

Famous Finds
CHAD
ETHIOPIA
TANZANIA

- **1960** At Olduvai Gorge, Tanzania, Louis Leakey finds 2-million-year-old **stone tools.**
- **1974** In Ethiopia, Donald Johanson finds "Lucy," a 3.5-million-year-old **hominid skeleton.**
- **1978** At Laetoli, Tanzania, Mary Leakey finds 3.6-million-year-old **hominid footprints.**
- **1994** In Ethiopia, an international team of scientists finds 2.33-million-year-old **hominid jaw.**
- **2002** In Chad, scientists announce discovery of a possible 6-million-year-old **hominid skull.**

GEOGRAPHY SKILLBUILDER: Interpreting Maps
1. **Movement** To what continents did Homo erectus groups migrate after leaving Africa?
2. **Human-Environment Interaction** What do the migration routes of Homo sapiens reveal about their survival skills and ability to adapt?

10 Chapter 1

Taking Notes

A history journal can act as a resource for you as you read your history text. Use a history journal to:

- outline a section or chapter as you read;
- copy graphic organizers from the text and add details as they are revealed;
- write down ideas and questions that occur to you as you read;
- record your reactions to people, events, and ideas from history.

Name _____ Date _____

GUIDED READING *Human Origins in Africa*

A. *Categorizing* As you read about early humans, fill in the chart below by describing the physical traits and achievements of each species of hominid listed.

Name	Traits	Achievements
1. Australopithecines		
2. *Homo habilis*		
3. *Homo erectus*		
4. Neanderthals		
5. Cro-Magnons		

B. *Comparing and Contrasting* Fill in the chart below to compare the Old Stone Age and the New Stone Age.

Stone Age	Began	Ended	Achievements
Paleolithic Age			
Neolithic Age			

C. *Writing for a Specific Purpose* On the back of this paper, explain the work of anthropologists, archaeologists, and paleontologists. Use the following terms in your explanation.

artifacts   **culture**   **technology**

Name _____   Date _____

GUIDED READING *Humans Try to Control Nature*

A. *Summarizing* As you read this section, take notes to answer questions about the development of agriculture.

People of the Old Stone Age were nomads who wandered from place to place in search of food.

1. How did hunter-gatherers use technology to improve their chances of survival?	2. What types of art did Paleolithic people create?

About 10,000 years ago, an agricultural revolution began.

3. What factors led to the agricultural revolution?	4. How did farming develop and spread worldwide?

Farming led to a settled way of life.

5. What were some of the cultural achievements of Neolithic villagers?	6. What problems did early villagers face?

B. *Identifying Problems and Solutions* On the back of this paper explain how stone age peoples used **slash-and-burn farming** and the **domestication** of animals to produce a steady source of food.

CHAPTER
1
Section 3

GUIDED READING *Patterns of Change: Civilization*

A. *Determining Main Ideas* As you read this section, fill in the boxes below. List the social and economic changes that led to the development of cities and the rise of civilization.

Village and town life begin.

1. Economic changes	2. Social changes

Cities emerge and grow.

3. Economic changes	4. Social changes

Civilizations arise.

B. *Writing Expository Paragraphs* On the back of this paper, explain how Ur typified an ancient civilization. Use the following terms in your explanation.

specialization	artisans	institution	scribes
cuneiform	barter	ziggurat	

Name _____   Date _____

CHAPTER 1   BUILDING VOCABULARY *The Peopling of the World*

A. *Matching* Match the description in the second column with the term or name in the first column. Write the appropriate letter next to the word.

_____ 1. artifact

_____ 2. Paleolithic Age

_____ 3. Neolithic Age

_____ 4. *Homo sapiens*

_____ 5. hunter-gatherer

_____ 6. artisan

_____ 7. scribe

_____ 8. Bronze Age

a. skilled worker who makes goods by hand

b. the New Stone Age, in which people learned to grow crops and raise animals

c. group whose food supply depends on hunting animals and collecting plant foods

d. the earlier and longer part of the Stone Age, in which tools were invented

e. period of time when people began making bronze tools and weapons

f. the species name for modern humans

g. human-made object

h. professional record-keeper

B. *Completion* Select the term or name that best completes the sentence.

culture	Neolithic	farming	barter
hominid	Revolution	cuneiform	ziggurat
nomad	slash-and-burn		

1. A _____ moves from place to place searching for new sources of food.

2. Ancient Sumerians practiced _____ when they traded goods and services without using money.

3. Sumerian scribes invented _____, a system of writing using wedge-shaped symbols.

4. A people's unique way of life is called _____.

5. The beginnings of farming that characterized the _____ brought far-reaching changes in human life.

6. In _____, people cut trees or grasses and burn them to clear fields for planting crops.

C. *Writing* Write a paragraph summarizing how early civilizations developed using the following terms.

technology	domestication	specialization	institution

Name _____ Date _____

CHAPTER 1

Section 1

SKILLBUILDER PRACTICE *Interpreting Maps*

The map on page 10 of your textbook shows early human migration routes. To interpret the information depicted in the map, first study the compass rose, scale, and legend. The compass rose shows direction, the scale indicates distance, and the legend explains what the colors and symbols represent. Then answer the questions below. (See Skillbuilder Handbook)

1. In what directions did *Homo erectus* migrate from Kenya in east Africa to Indonesia? _____

_____

2. To what continents did *Homo sapiens* migrate from Asia? _____

_____

3. What is the approximate distance *Homo erectus* traveled as they migrated from Ubeidiya, Israel, to Lantian, China? _____

_____

4. What environmental factors may have influenced migration routes? _____

_____

5. a. On what continents are fossil sites of *Homo erectus* located? _____

_____

   b. On what continents are there fossil sites of *Homo sapiens*? _____

_____

   c. What do the dates of these sites reveal about the chronology of early human migration? _____

_____

6. What conclusions can you draw about early humans from the information presented in the map? _____

_____

CHAPTER 1

Section 2

GEOGRAPHY APPLICATION: PLACE *Catal Huyuk*

Directions: Read the paragraphs below and study the illustration carefully. Then answer the questions that follow.

Among the many ancient settlements of human beings in the world was the village of Catal Huyuk. Founded approximately 8,000 years ago in the hills of what is now Turkey, Catal Huyuk lasted for nearly 2,000 years before mysteriously disappearing.

The settlement was the world's most advanced human center of the first agricultural age. However, Catal Huyuk did not develop near a major river system, as might have been expected of a farming village. Instead, it developed near a small stream in the shadow of three menacing volcanoes.

The people of Catal Huyuk fortified themselves against invaders and wild animals by building a village that contained no doors or streets. Instead, inhabitants used a hole in the roof to enter and exit and people simply moved around on top of each other's dwellings. Families constructed their houses with strong mud-dried brick. The roofs were made of woven reeds and mud and were connected on one or more sides to the units next to them. Each family dwelling contained an open hearth, an oven in the wall, and clearly defined sleeping areas.

The residents of Catal Huyuk appeared to be a religious people. Elaborate shrines were constructed in the same fashion as the dwellings, and contained four or five rooms. Paintings filled the walls of these shrines and often included the chief deity, who was believed to be a goddess. This goddess was frequently depicted giving birth, nursing a child, or living as an old woman accompanied by a vulture.

The economic base of Catal Huyuk was also highly sophisticated for the time. Like their ancestors, these people still hunted, but they also bred goats, sheep, and cattle. In addition, they produced many different types of foods, including peas, several grains, berries, and berry wine. However, like other prehistoric humans, the people of Catal Huyuk did not live much past their twenties.

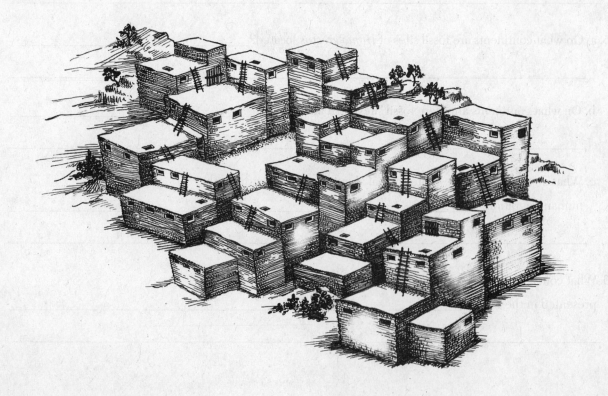

Interpreting Text and Visuals

1. What does the illustration reveal about the way that the people of Catal Huyuk entered their dwellings and moved from house to house? _____

_____

2. Where was Catal Huyuk located? _____

3. Describe the physical surroundings of Catal Huyuk. _____

_____

4. Explain how the village of Catal Huyuk was constructed. _____

_____

_____

_____

5. What role did religion play in the lives of the people of Catal Huyuk? _____

_____

_____

6. If Catal Huyuk had been built near a major river system, how might life have been different?

_____

_____

_____

7. Look again at the illustration. Explain what you think the inhabitants of Catal Huyuk gained by constructing their settlement in this manner. _____

_____

_____

_____

_____

CHAPTER 1

Section 1

PRIMARY SOURCE *from Lucy: The Beginnings of Humankind*

In the following excerpt, American paleoanthropologist Donald Johanson describes how he and his colleague Tom Gray found the fossils of a 3.5 million-year-old hominid they nicknamed "Lucy." As you read, consider how the scientists feel about their discovery.

On the morning of November 30, 1974, I woke, as I usually do on a field expedition, at day-break. I was in Ethiopia, camped on the edge of a small muddy river, the Awash, at a place called Hadar, about a hundred miles northeast of Addis Ababa. I had been there for several weeks, acting as coleader of a group of scientists looking for fossils.

. . . It was still relatively cool, not more than 80 degrees. The air had the unmistakable crystalline smell of early morning on the desert, faintly touched with the smoke of cooking fires. Some of the Afar tribesmen who worked for the expedition had brought their families with them, and there was a small compound of dome-shaped huts made of sticks and grass mats about two hundred yards from the main camp. . . .

Tom Gray joined me for coffee. Tom was an American graduate student who had come out to Hadar to study the fossil animals and plants of the region, to reconstruct as accurately as possible the kinds and frequencies and relationships of what had lived there at various times in the remote past and what the climate had been like. My own target—the reason for our expedition—was hominid fossils: the bones of extinct human ancestors and their close relatives. I was interested in the evidence for human evolution. But to understand that, to interpret any hominid fossils we might find, we had to have the supporting work of other specialists like Tom.

"So, what's up for today?" I asked.

Tom said he was busy marking fossil sites on a map.

"When are you going to mark in Locality 162?"

"I'm not sure where 162 is," he said.

"Then I guess I'll have to show you." I wasn't eager to go out with Gray that morning. I had a tremendous amount of work to catch up on. . . . I should have stayed in camp that morning—but I didn't. I felt a strong subconscious urge to go with

Tom, and I obeyed it. I wrote a note to myself in my daily diary: Nov. 30, 1974. To Locality 162 with Gray in A.M. Feel good.

As a paleoanthropologist—one who studies the fossils of human ancestors—I am superstitious. Many of us are, because the work we do depends a great deal on luck. The fossils we study are extremely rare, and quite a few distinguished paleo-anthropologists have gone a lifetime without finding a single one. I am one of the more fortunate. This was only my third year in the field at Hadar, and I had already found several. I know I am lucky, and I don't try to hide it. That is why I wrote "feel good" in my diary.

. . . Gray and I got into one of the expedition's four Land-Rovers and slowly jounced our way to Locality 162. . . . Although the spot we were head-ed for was only about four miles from camp, it took us half an hour to get there because of the rough terrain. When we arrived it was already beginning to get hot. . . .

Gray and I parked the Land-Rover on the slope of [a gully.] We were careful to face it in such a way that the canvas water bag that was hanging from the side mirror was in the shade. Gray plotted the locality on the map. Then we got out and began doing what most members of the expedition spent a great deal of their time doing: we began surveying, walking slowly about, looking for exposed fossils.

Some people are good at finding fossils. Others are hopelessly bad at it. It's a matter of practice, of training your eye to see what you need to see. I will never be as good as some of the Afar people. They spend all their time wandering around in the rocks and sand. They have to be sharp-eyed; their lives depend on it. Anything the least bit unusual they notice. . . .

Tom and I surveyed for a couple of hours. It was now close to noon, and the temperature was approaching 110. We hadn't found much. . . .

"I've had it," said Tom. "When do we head back to camp?"

"Right now. But let's go back this way and survey the bottom of that little gully over there."

The gully in question was just over the crest of the rise where we had been working all morning. It had been thoroughly checked out at least twice before by other workers, who had found nothing interesting. Nevertheless, conscious of the "lucky" feeling that had been with me since I woke, I decided to make that small final detour. There was virtually no bone in the gully. But as we turned to leave, I noticed something lying on the ground partway up the slope.

"That's a bit of a hominid arm," I said.

"Can't be. It's too small. Has to be a monkey of some kind."

We knelt to examine it.

"Much too small," said Gray again.

I shook my head. "Hominid."

"What makes you so sure?" he said.

"That piece right next to your hand. That's hominid too."

. . .He picked it up. It was the back of a small skull. A few feet away was part of a femur: a thighbone. . . . We stood up, and began to see other bits of bone on the slope: a couple of vertebrae, part of a pelvis—all of them hominid. An unbelievable, impermissible thought flickered through my mind. Suppose all these fitted together? Could they be parts of a single, extremely primitive skeleton? No such skeleton had ever been found—anywhere.

"Look at that," said Gray. "Ribs."

A single individual?

"I can't believe it," I said. "I just can't believe it."

"By God, you'd better believe it!" shouted Gray. "Here it is. Right here!" His voice went up into a howl. I joined him. In that 110-degree heat we began jumping up and down. With nobody to share our feelings, we hugged each other, sweaty and smelly, howling and hugging in the heat-shimmering gravel. . . .

"We've got to stop jumping around," I finally said. "We may step on something. Also, we've got to make sure."

"Aren't you sure . . . ?"

"I mean, suppose we find two left legs. There may be several individuals here, all mixed up. Let's play it cool until we can come back and make absolutely sure that it all fits together."

We collected a couple of pieces of jaw, marked the spot exactly and got into the blistering Land-Rover for the run back to camp. On the way we picked up two expedition geologists who were loaded down with rock samples they had been gathering.

"Something big," Gray kept saying to them. "Something big. Something big."

"Cool it," I said.

But about a quarter of a mile from camp, Gray could not cool it. He pressed his thumb on the Land-Rover's horn, and the long blast brought a scurry of scientists who had been bathing in the river. "We've got it," he yelled. " . . . We've got it. We've got The Whole Thing!"

That afternoon everyone in camp was at the gully, sectioning off the site and preparing for a massive collecting job that ultimately took three weeks. When it was done, we had recovered several hundred pieces of bone (many of them fragments) representing about forty percent of the skeleton of a single individual. Tom's and my original hunch had been right. There was no bone duplication.

But a single individual of what? On preliminary examination it was very hard to say, for nothing quite like it had ever been discovered. The camp was rocking with excitement. That first night we never went to bed at all. We talked and talked. We drank beer after beer. There was a tape recorder in the camp, and a tape of the Beatles song "Lucy in the Sky with Diamonds" went belting out into the night sky, and was played at full volume over and over again out of sheer exuberance. At some point during that unforgettable evening—I no longer remember exactly when—the new fossil picked up the name of Lucy, and has been so known ever since, although its proper name—its acquisition number in the Hadar collection—is AL 288-1.

from Donald C. Johanson and Maitland A. Edey, *Lucy: The Beginnings of Humankind* (New York: Simon and Schuster, 1981), 13–18.

Discussion Questions

1. ***Summarizing*** Where did Johanson and Gray find Lucy?
2. ***Making Inferences*** Why do you think Johanson and Gray felt that they had discovered "something big"?
3. ***Drawing Conclusions*** What important clues do you think fossils like Lucy provide about the past?

Name _____ Date _____

PRIMARY SOURCE Lascaux Cave Painting

A prehistoric artist painted this bull in the Lascaux Cave in France. What can this cave painting tell you about prehistoric life?

Copyright © R. Sheridan/Ancient Art & Architecture Collection.

Research Options

1. *Interpreting Visual Sources* Find and compare photographs of cave paintings like this one that have been found in France, Spain, South America, and Africa. What do these paintings have in common? How are they different? With classmates, create a bulletin board display to illustrate a variety of Stone Age art.

Using Research in Writing

2. Find out more about how prehistoric artists made their cave paintings. What tools did they use? How did they make colored paints? Share your findings with classmates.

3. Cave art provides important clues to prehistoric life. With a partner, research what is being done to protect and preserve cave paintings.

CHAPTER
1

Section 2

PRIMARY SOURCE *from* "Window on the Stone Age"
by Leon Jaroff

In December 1994 Jean-Marie Chauvet and two fellow cave explorers discovered Stone Age cave paintings in southeastern France. As you read this account, think about the significance of their discovery.

At the base of a cliff in the Ardèche region in southeastern France last December, the three middle-aged spelunkers felt a breeze wafting from a pile of rock and debris. "That was a sign that there was a cave beneath it," recalls Jean-Marie Chauvet. With his companions, Chauvet cleared away an opening, then wriggled through a tunnel into a complex of large caves.

Then, in the pale glow of their head lamps, the explorers noticed two red lines on a cavern wall. Chauvet, a government employee who oversees the protection of the many historically important caves in the region, recognized the markings as "characteristic of the Stone Age." What he did not immediately realize—and the world did not know until the French Culture Ministry announced it last week—was that they had discovered an archaeological trove that may rival even the fabled drawings on the cave walls at Lascaux in France and Altamira in Spain. The spelunkers had found an extraordinarily clear window on prehistoric life. . . . Probing deeper into the cavern system, they began coming upon exquisite, intricately detailed wall paintings and engravings of animals, as well as numerous images of human hands, some in red, others in black pigment. "I thought I was dreaming," says Chauvet. "We were all covered with goose pimples."

The art was in pristine condition, apparently undisturbed for up to 20,000 years, as was other evidence of the ancient artists' presence: flint knives, mounds of clay used for making paint, and charred fire pits.

Photographs of the Stone Age art show images of lions, bison, deer, bears, horses and some 50 woolly rhinos. "These paintings are more beautiful than those in Lascaux," says Patrice Béghain, the regional head of cultural affairs. "There is a sense of rhythm and texture that is truly remarkable." . . .

Of particular interest to Jean Clottes, France's foremost expert on prehistoric rock art, is the fact that, in contrast to previous cave artwork, images of predatory and dangerous species—bears, lions, rhinos, a panther and a hyena—far outnumber the horses, bison, deer and mammoths usually hunted by Stone Age people. "The paintings in this cave," he says, "will force us to change how we interpret Stone Age art."

Béghain is particularly struck by the skull of a bear perched on a stone near a wall adorned by an ursine image. "What is significant," says the official, "is that some 17,000 to 20,000 years ago, a human being decided to put it in that particular place for a particular reason. I think it fair to assume that the bear did not self-decapitate on that spot to intrigue us." Was this an altar for some Paleolithic ceremony?

Stung by lessons learned at Altamira and Lascaux, where initial unrestricted access to the caves obliterated archaeological clues and led to the rapid deterioration of artwork, the French Culture Ministry has put the Chauvet cave off limits to all but a handful of experts and installed video surveillance cameras and police guards at the entrance. "Our goal," says Béghain, "is to keep the cave in this virgin state so that research can, in theory, continue indefinitely." —Reported by Bruce Crumley/Paris

from *Time*, January 30, 1995, 80–81.

Activity Options

1. ***Writing Narrative Paragraphs*** Imagine that you are Jean-Marie Chauvet. Write a diary entry about your discovery and share it with classmates.

2. ***Forming and Supporting Opinions*** With your classmates, hold an informal debate about whether the public should or should not have unlimited access to the Chauvet cave. Draw on information in your textbook and on independent research on cave art to prepare your argument.

CHAPTER 1

Section 1

LITERATURE SELECTION *from The Clan of the Cave Bear*
by Jean M. Auel

In her novel The Clan of the Cave Bear, *American writer Jean M. Auel describes
how a group of humans on the dry grassy plains of Russia may have lived about
30,000 years ago. As you read this excerpt, notice how Brun, Iza, and Creb—
members of the Clan of the Cave Bear—look, dress, speak, and act.*

The band of travelers crossed the river just beyond the waterfall where it widened and foamed around rocks jutting up through the shallow water. They were twenty in number, young and old. The clan had totaled twenty-six before the earthquake that destroyed their cave. Two men led the way, far in front of a knot of women and children flanked by a couple of older men. Younger men trailed behind.

They followed the broad stream as it began its braided, meandering course across the flat steppes, and watched the carrion birds circling. Flying scavengers usually meant that whatever had attracted their attention was still alive. The men in the lead hurried to investigate. A wounded animal was easy prey for hunters, providing no four-legged predators had similar ideas.

A woman, midway along in her first pregnancy, walked in front of the rest of the women. She saw the two men in the lead glance at the ground and move on. It must be a meat eater, she thought. The clan seldom ate carnivorous animals.

She was just over four and a half feet tall, large boned, stocky, and bow-legged, but walked upright on strong muscular legs and flat bare feet. Her arms, long in proportion to her body, were bowed like her legs. She had a large beaky nose, a prognathous jaw jutting out like a muzzle, and no chin. Her low forehead sloped back into a long, large head, resting on a short, thick neck. At the back of her head was a boney knob, an occipital bun, that emphasized its length.

A soft down of short brown hair, tending to curl, covered her legs and shoulders and ran along the upper spine of her back. It thickened into a head of heavy, long, rather bushy hair. She was already losing her winter pallor to a summer tan. Big, round, intelligent, dark brown eyes were deep set below overhanging brow ridges, and they were filled with curiosity as she quickened her pace to see what the man had passed by.

The woman was old for a first pregnancy, nearly twenty, and the clan thought she was barren until the life stirring within her started to show. The load she carried had not been lightened because she was pregnant, however. She had a large basket strapped to her back, with bundles tied behind, hanging below, and piled on top of it. Several drawstring bags dangled from a thong, which was wrapped around the pliable hide she wore in such a way as to produce folds and pouches for carrying things. One bag was particularly distinctive. It was made from an otter hide, obviously so because it had been cured with its waterproof fur, feet, tail, and head left intact.

Rather than a slit in the skin of the animal's belly, only the throat had been cut to provide an opening to remove the innards, flesh, and bones, leaving a pouchlike bag. The head, attached by a strip of skin at the back, was the cover flap, and a red-dyed cord of sinew was threaded through holes punched around the neck opening, drawn tight, and tied to the thong at her waist.

When the woman first saw the creature the men had left behind, she was puzzled by what appeared to be an animal without fur. But when she drew closer, she gasped and stepped back a pace, clutching the small leather pouch around her neck in an unconscious gesture to ward off unknown spirits. She fingered the small objects inside her amulet through the leather, invoking protection, and leaned forward to look closer, hesitant to take a step, but not quite able to believe she saw what she thought she was seeing.

Her eyes had not deceived her. It was not an animal that had drawn the voracious birds. It was a child, a gaunt, strange-looking child!

The woman looked around, wondering what other fearful enigmas might be nearby, and started to skirt the unconscious child, but she heard a moan. The woman stopped and, forgetting her fears, knelt beside the child and shook her gently. The medicine woman reached to untie the cord that held the otter-skin bag closed as soon as she saw the festering claw marks and swollen leg when the girl rolled over.

The man in the lead glanced back and saw the woman kneeling beside the child. He walked back to them.

"Iza! Come!" he commanded. "Cave lion tracks and scat ahead."

"It's a child, Brun. Hurt but not dead," she replied.

Brun looked at the thin young girl with the high forehead, small nose, and strangely flat face. "Not Clan," the leader gestured abruptly and turned to walk away.

"Brun, she's a child. She's hurt. She'll die if we leave her here." Iza's eyes pleaded as she made the hand signals.

The leader of the small clan stared down at the imploring woman. He was much bigger than she, over five feet tall, heavily muscled and powerful, with a deep barrel chest and thick bowed legs. The cast of his features was similar, though more pro-nounced—heavier supraorbital ridges, larger nose. His legs, stomach, chest, and upper back were cov-ered with a coarse brown hair that was not enough to be called a pelt, but not far from it. A bushy beard hid his chinless jutting jaw. His wrap was similar, too, but not as full, cut shorter, and tied differently, with fewer folds and pouches for holding things.

He carried no burdens, only his outer fur wrap, suspended on his back by a wide band of leather wrapped around his sloping forehead, and his weapons. On his right thigh was a scar, blackened like a tattoo, shaped roughly like a U with the tops flaring outward, the mark of his totem, the bison. He needed no mark or ornament to identify his leadership. His bearing and the deference of the others made his position clear.

He shifted his club, the long foreleg of a horse, from his shoulder to the ground, supporting the handle with his thigh, and Iza knew he was giving her plea serious consideration. She waited quietly, hiding her agitation, to give him time to think.

Brun didn't like making quick decisions about anything unusual that might affect his clan, espe-cially now when they were homeless, and he resist-ed the impulse to refuse at once. I should have known Iza would want to help her, he thought; she's even used her healing magic on animals some-times, especially young ones. She'll be upset if I don't let her help this child. Clan or Others, it makes no difference, all she can see is a child who

is hurt. Well, maybe that's what makes her a good medicine woman.

But medicine woman or not, she is just a woman. What difference will it make if she's upset? Iza knows better than to show it, and we have enough problems without a wounded stranger. But her totem will know, all the spirits will. Would it make them more angry if she's upset? If we find a cave . . . no, when we find a new cave, Iza will have to make her drink for the cave ceremony. What if she's so upset she makes a mistake? Angry spirits could make it go wrong, and they're angry enough already. Nothing must go wrong with the ceremony for the new cave.

Let her take the child, he thought. She'll soon get tired of carrying the extra load, and the girl is so far gone, not even my sibling's magic may be strong enough to save her. Brun shrugged noncom-mittally. It was up to her; Iza could take the girl with them or not as she pleased. He turned and strode off.

Iza reached into her basket and pulled out a leather cloak. She wrapped it around the girl, hoist-ed her up, and secured the unconscious child to her hip with the aid of the supple hide, surprised at how little she weighed for her height. The girl moaned as she was lifted and Iza patted her reas-suringly, then fell into place behind the two men.

The other women had stopped, holding back from the encounter between Iza and Brun. When they saw the medicine woman pick something up and take it with her, their hands flew in rapid motions punctuated by a few guttural sounds, dis-cussing it with excited curiosity. Except for the otter-skin pouch, they were dressed the same as Iza, and as heavily burdened. Among them they carried all the clan's worldly possessions, those that had been salvaged from the rubble after the quake.

Two of the seven women carried babies in a fold of their wraps next to their skin, convenient for nurs-ing. While they were waiting, one felt a drop of warm wetness, whipped her naked infant out of the fold, and held it in front of her until it was through wetting. When they weren't traveling, babies were often wrapped in soft swaddling skins. To absorb moisture and soft milky stools, any of several materi-als were packed around them: fleece from wild sheep gathered from thorny shrubs when the mou-flon were shedding, down from birds' breasts, or fuzz from fibrous plants. But while they traveled, it was easier and simpler to carry babies naked and, without missing a step, let them mess on the ground.

. . . An older girl, not yet a woman but carrying a woman's load, walked behind the woman who followed Iza, glancing back now and then at a boy, very nearly a man, trailing the women. He tried to allow enough distance between himself and them so it would seem he was one of the three hunters bringing up the rear and not one of the children. He wished he had game to carry, too, and even envied the old man, one of the two flanking the women, who carried a large hare over his shoulder, felled by a stone from his sling.

The hunters were not the only source of food for the clan. The women often contributed the greater share, and their sources were more reliable. Despite their burdens, they foraged as they traveled, and so efficiently it hardly slowed them down. A patch of day lilies was quickly stripped of buds and flowers, and tender new roots exposed with a few strokes of the digging sticks. Cattail roots, pulled loose from beneath the surface of marshy backwaters, were even easier to gather.

If they hadn't been on the move, the women would have made a point of remembering the location of the tall stalky plants, to return later in the season to pick the tender tails at the top for a vegetable. Later still, yellow pollen mixed with starch pounded from the fibers of old roots would make doughy unleavened biscuits. When the tops dried, fuzz would be collected; and several of the baskets were made from the tough leaves and stalks. Now they gathered only what they found, but little was overlooked.

New shoots and tender young leaves of clover, alfalfa, dandelion; thistles stripped of prickles before they were cut down; a few early berries and fruits. The pointed digging sticks were in constant use; nothing was safe from them in the women's deft hands. . . . Though the selection would be more varied later in the summer, food was plentiful—if one knew where to look.

Iza looked up when an old man, past thirty, hobbled up to her after they were on their way again. He carried neither burden nor weapon, only a long staff to help him walk. His right leg was crippled and smaller than the left, yet he managed to move with surprising agility.

His right shoulder and upper arm were atrophied and the shriveled arm had been amputated below the elbow. The powerful shoulder and arm and muscular leg of his fully developed left side

made him appear lopsided. His huge cranium was even larger than those of the rest of the clan, and the difficulty of his birth had caused the defect that crippled him for life.

He was also a sibling of Iza and Brun, first-born, and would have been leader but for his affliction. He wore a leather wrap cut in the masculine style and carried his warm outer fur, which was also used as a sleeping fur, on his back as the other men did. But he had several pouches hanging from his waist thong and a cloak similar to the kind the women used which held a large bulging object to his back.

The left side of his face was hideously scarred and his left eye was missing, but his good right eye sparkled with intelligence, and something more. For all his hobbling, he moved with a grace that came from great wisdom and a sureness of his place within the clan. He was Mog-ur, the most powerful magician, most awesome and revered holy man of all the clans. He was convinced that his wasted body was given to him so that he could take his place as intermediary with the spirit world rather than at the head of his clan. In many ways he had more power than any leader, and he knew it. Only close relatives remembered his birth name and called him by it.

"Creb," Iza said in greeting and acknowledged his appearance with a motion that meant she was pleased he had joined her.

"Iza?" he questioned with a gesture toward the child she carried. The woman opened her cloak and Creb looked closely at the small flushed face. The girl moaned, and Creb's expression softened. He nodded his approval.

"Good," he said. The word was gruff, guttural. Then he made a sign that meant, "Enough have died."

Discussion Questions

1. *Describing Character* What do men and women from the Clan of the Cave Bear look like? Describe their physical characteristics and clothing.
2. *Determining Main Ideas* What food do clan members eat, and how do they obtain it?
3. *Drawing Conclusions* Why do Brun and the other men leave the injured girl behind?
4. *Making Inferences* How similar or different is Auel's portrayal of Stone Age life from that of present-day life in the United States?

CHAPTER 1 Section 1

HISTORYMAKERS Mary Leakey
Digger into the Past

"I never felt interpretation was my job. What I came to do was to dig things up and take them out as well as I could. There is so much we do not know, and the more we do know, the more we realize that early interpretations were completely wrong."—Mary Leakey

Mary Leakey gained fame for two reasons. She was extremely skillful—and she had incredible luck. Brian Fagan, a well-known archaeologist, praised the "fierce determination and passion for detail" she showed when working in the field. She also made spectacular finds, maybe because of what people called "Leakey luck." The daughter of an artist, Mary Douglas Nicol showed skill at drawing when she was young. She also showed a rebellious nature; in fact, two different schools expelled her. As a teen, she began to combine her ability to draw with her interest in prehistoric people. She joined archaeological digs and sketched the objects that scientists found.

Luck changed Mary's life in 1933. At a London dinner party, she was introduced to Louis Leakey. A paleoanthropologist—someone who studies humanlike creatures that predate human beings—Leakey, whom she eventually married, asked her to illustrate a book with drawings of fossils he had discovered in Africa. Two years later they traveled to Africa, which, Mary later said, "cast its spell" on her. For the next few decades the Leakeys worked together, trying to understand human origins.

They made an excellent team. Their son Richard Leakey, himself a famous naturalist, summed up their talents. "She was much more organized and structured and much more of a technician. He was much more excitable, a magician." Louis traveled the world, lecturing on his theories and working to raise money for more digs. Meanwhile Mary, though never formally trained in the field, stayed in Africa to supervise the work.

Mary did more than just lead digs. Over the years, she made several major finds. The first came in 1948. She found the fossil remains of a creature that the Leakeys named Proconsul. This animal is a common ancestor of apes and humans.

Another discovery came in 1959. Louis was ill one day and had to stay in camp. Mary went fossil hunting with her two dogs for company and she found a small piece of bone jutting out of the ground. She raced back to tell Louis that she had found an early hominid. "I've got him!" she said. Working with dental picks and delicate brushes, they unearthed nearly 400 pieces of bone. Carefully piecing together the puzzle, they assembled the skull of a humanlike creature. Then "Leakey luck" struck again. A camera crew reached the camp the day after the discovery. Their film helped spread the news quickly, and the Leakeys became famous. Soon they received more money to continue their work. A few years later, Mary found another hominid creature and named this specimen *Homo habilis,* which means "able man."

In 1972, Louis died and Mary added public lecturing and fundraising to her work in the field. However, she tried to avoid the heated debates over human origins. Her role, she thought, was simply to find fossils. She once described the attraction of her work: "For me it was the sheer instinctive joy of collecting, or indeed one could say treasure hunting."

In 1978, Mary made perhaps her greatest find. While some members of her team were playing near their camp, one found fossilized animal prints in the dirt. Under Mary's leadership, they carefully cleaned a large area. Their efforts revealed a remarkable find: the footprints of two, and perhaps three, hominids who had walked upright. "Now this," Mary told the team, "is really something to put on the mantelpiece."

Five years later, Mary Leakey finally retired from the field. She continued with her artwork and writing until her death in 1996. She had lived, as a former colleague said, "an extraordinary life."

Questions

1. *Comparing and Contrasting* How did Louis and Mary Leakey balance each other with their special talents?
2. *Determining Main Ideas* What major finds did Mary Leakey make?
3. *Drawing Conclusions* What did she like about studying human origins?

HISTORYMAKERS The Iceman
Frozen in Time

"I needed only one second to see that the body was [at least] 4,000 years old."—archaeologist Konrad Spindler

Two storms and two walks in the mountains combined to give archaeologists one of their most treasured finds in recent history. Around 3000 B.C., a lone man was walking through the Alps, a mountain range in south-central Europe. For some reason, he lay down to rest. While he was sleeping, a sudden storm dropped snow on him, and he froze to death. Yet the blanket of snow that caused his death preserved the man's body for thousands of years. It cushioned him from the great weight of the Alps' glaciers as they moved over his resting place.

In recent years warmer weather has melted those glaciers, revealing the snow underneath. Then, in the fall of 1991, came the second storm—a dust storm in the Sahara Desert, far away in Africa. It was so large that dust blew north to the Alps. The dust absorbed the heat of the sun, causing the snow to melt. Days later, a German couple strolled along this mountain trail and saw a human head and shoulders. After a long undisturbed rest, the Iceman was revealed to the world.

An archaeologist later commented on the timing of the couple's walk. "We think [the Iceman] was found only three days after he had melted out," the scientist said, "and three days later, the snow fell again—enough to have buried him. He was out of the ice, then, only six days, at maximum."

At first, no one knew what a treasure the Iceman was. Some thought he was a modern mountain climber who had died of the cold. Police tried to remove the body using a jackhammer, which tore away a piece of the Iceman's hip. Workers finally pried the body out using ski poles and wooden sticks. Then archaeologist Konrad Spindler arrived. Seeing a copper ax found with the body, Spindler realized that the Iceman could be thousands of years old. He also saw that contact with the air had caused fungus to grow on the body. He ordered the mummy placed in a freezer to save it for further study.

As the scientists examined the body, local people named him. Ötzi, they called him, after the nearby Ötztal Valley. He was five feet two inches tall and had brown curly hair. He had tattoo marks on his back, one kneecap, and one foot. Since all these areas would have been covered by clothing, scientists think the tattoos were not decorations but had spiritual meaning. His pants and jacket were made from the skin of animals. He also wore a long cape made of grass. His leather shoes had been stuffed with grass to help keep his feet warm in the cold mountains. In the tatters of his clothing, the scientists spotted some grains of wheat that grew only at low altitudes. The few pieces of charcoal he carried were made of trees that now grow in a valley just a few hours walk to the south.

Scientists also studied his tools. The Iceman had a six-foot long bow that had not yet been strung. He carried 14 arrows, two of which had stone arrowheads and feathers. His deerskin quiver excited the scientists—they had never seen such an object from this period. He carried a small stone-point knife and several pieces of flint that were ready to be sharpened into arrowheads or other points. A long stick ended in a piece of deer antler. Scientists think it was used to sharpen the flint into points. He had a backpack and carried two mushrooms that are known to have value as medicines. Most spectacular was the Iceman's ax. It had a wooden handle that curved at the top, where notches were made to fit the ax blade. The blade itself was solid copper, putting the Iceman in the period archaeologists call the Copper Age.

Scientists continue to work on the Iceman and his tools. They keep Ötzi's body frozen to preserve it, only removing it from the freezer for periods of 20 minutes at a time. As the scientists revisit this remarkable mummy, though, they add more and more to our understanding of the human past.

Questions

Determining Main Ideas

1. How was the body revealed?
2. How did the Iceman try to protect himself from the cold?
3. ***Drawing Conclusions*** Based on the evidence, what could you say about the Iceman's diet?

Name _____ Date _____

CHAPTER 1

Section 3

CONNECTIONS ACROSS TIME AND CULTURES
From Ancient to Modern Communities

Early cities like Ur were both similar to and different from their modern-day counterparts. Compare your community with ancient Ur by answering the following questions.

1. Farmers, artisans, and merchants were the economic job base in Ur. What types of jobs are the economic base of your community? _____

_____

2. How would a physical description of your community differ from that of Ur? Consider street layout, homes, and businesses. _____

_____

3. Business and trade took place in a bazaar in Ur. How is a bazaar like a modern shopping mall? _____

_____

4. Fill in this chart to show how Ur and your community display the five characteristics of civilization.

Characteristic	Ur	Your Community
Advanced cities		
Specialized workers		
Record keeping		
Complex institutions		
Advanced technology		

Name _____ Date _____

CHAPTER 1
Section 1

RETEACHING ACTIVITY *Human Origins in Africa*

Determining Main Ideas
The following questions deal with the development of a culture. Answer them in the space provided.

1. What do anthropologists mean when they use the term *culture*?

_____

_____

2. What are some common practices that a culture shares?

_____

_____

3. What are some examples of the social organization of a culture?

_____

_____

4. From what institutions or groups in a society do individuals learn their culture?

_____

_____

Reading Comprehension
Find the name or term in the second column that best matches the description in the first column. Then write the letter of your answer in the blank.

5. _____ human-made objects

6. _____ humans and other creatures that walk upright

7. _____ another name for the Old Stone Age

8. _____ ways of applying knowledge, tools, and inventions to meet human needs

9. _____ species name for modern humans

10. _____ famous discovery of cave paintings

a. technology

b. hominids

c. *Homo sapiens*

d. Lascaux

e. Paleolithic Age

f. artifacts

Name _____ Date _____

Multiple Choice
Choose the best answer for each item. Write the letter of your answer in the blank.

____1. Highly mobile people who moved from place to place searching for new food sources were called
 a. neanderthals.
 b. hominids.
 c. nomads.
 d. farmers.

____2. People whose food supply depended on hunting animals and collecting plant foods were called
 a. nomads.
 b. a culture group.
 c. Cro-Magnons.
 d. hunter-gatherers.

____3. Discoveries of artistic works from early men and women include all of these *except*
 a. polished beads made from mammoth tusks.
 b. cave paintings.
 c. watercolor paintings.
 d. necklaces of seashells.

____4. Another name for the Neolithic Revolution is the
 a. industrial revolution.
 b. agricultural revolution.
 c. New Stone Age.
 d. technological revolution.

____5. Early farmers used slash-and-burn methods because
 a. the ashes fertilized the soil and brought renewed growth after a few years.
 b. they didn't want their neighbors to be able to use the land.
 c. it produced the largest crops in the shortest period of time.
 d. lack of rain made it the only method possible.

____6. The taming of animals in order to raise them as a constant source of food was known as
 a. the agricultural revolution.
 b. domestication.
 c. herding.
 d. ranching.

____7. The agricultural village known as Catal Huyuk was best known for its
 a. obsidian products.
 b. religious artifacts.
 c. fossilized animal skeletons.
 d. strong social organization.

____8. One drawback to the new settled way of life of people in villages such as Catal Huyuk was
 a. boredom.
 b. crowded conditions.
 c. easily spread diseases.
 d. overproduction of food.

CHAPTER 1

Section 3

RETEACHING ACTIVITY *Civilization*
Case Study: Ur in Sumer

Summarizing

Complete the chart below by summarizing information about the key characteristics of a civilization.

CHARACTERISTIC	EXPLANATION	EXAMPLE
Advanced cities	1.	2.
Specialized workers	3.	4.
Complex institutions	5.	6.
Record keeping	7.	8.
Improved technology	9.	10.

Reading Comprehension

Find the name or term in the second column that best matches the description in the first column. Then write the letter of your answer in the blank.

_____ 11. the development of skills in a specific kind of work

_____ 12. professional record keepers

_____ 13. the time when people began using a mixture of copper and tin to shape tools and weapons

_____ 14. a system of writing invented in Sumer

_____ 15. a way of trading goods and services without money

_____ 16. a pyramid-shaped, tiered monument found in Ur

a. ziggurat

b. scribes

c. cuneiform

d. Bronze Age

e. barter

f. specialization

Name _____ Date _____

CHAPTER 2
Section 1

GUIDED READING *City-States in Mesopotamia*

A. *Identifying Problems and Solutions* As you read about the Sumerians, fill in
the chart below to explain how they solved problems they faced.

The Problems	The Solutions
1. With flooding of the rivers unpredictable, how could farmers water their fields during the dry summer months?	
2. With no natural barriers, how could villagers protect themselves?	
3. With limited natural resources, how could Sumerians get the materials for tools and buildings?	
4. How should the Sumerian city-states be ruled?	
5. What could be done to please the gods and earn their protection in life?	

B. *Categorizing Facts and Details* List examples of Sumerian culture in the boxes below.

Religion	Literature	Architecture	Inventions

C. *Determining Word Meaning* On the back of this paper, identify **Hammurabi,**
the characteristics of an **empire,** and the process of **cultural diffusion**.

CHAPTER 2

Section 2

GUIDED READING *Pyramids on the Nile*

A. *Determing Main Ideas* As you read about ancient Egyptian civilization, fill out the chart below by writing notes to answer the questions.

Government	
1. Why is Narmer a legendary hero in ancient Egyptian history?	
2. How did the role of Egyptian pharaohs differ from the role of Mesopotamian rulers?	
3. Why did the Egyptians build great pyramids for their kings?	

Culture	
4. How did Egyptian religious beliefs compare with those of the Mesopotamians?	
5. What social classes made up Egyptian society?	
6. What were significant achievements of the ancient Egyptians in science and technology?	
7. How did the Egyptian writing system compare with the Mesopotamian system?	

B. *Writing Expository Paragraphs* On the back of this paper, write a paragraph explaining why ancient Egypt was viewed as the "gift of the Nile." Use the words **delta** and **cataract** in your writing.

Name _____ Date _____

GUIDED READING *Planned Cities on the Indus*

A. *Determining Main Ideas* As you read this section, list the key characteristics of the first Indian civilization in the web diagram below.

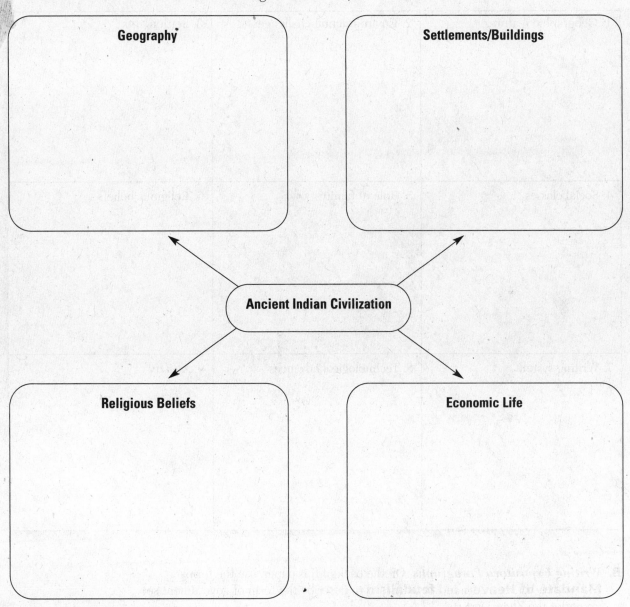

Geography

Settlements/Buildings

Ancient Indian Civilization

Religious Beliefs

Economic Life

B. *Drawing Conclusions* Explain how the **monsoons** affect the climate and in turn the people of the Indus Valley.

Early River Valley Civilizations 23

CHAPTER
2
Section 4

GUIDED READING *River Dynasties in China*

A. *Summarizing* As you read this section, fill out the chart below by describing key
features of ancient China under the Shang Dynasty.

1. Geographic features	2. Environmental challenges	3. Settlements
4. Social classes	5. Role of family	6. Religious beliefs
7. Writing system	8. Technological advances	9. Artistry

B. *Writing Expository Paragraphs* On the back of this paper, use the terms
Mandate of Heaven and **feudalism** to describe the form of government set
up under the Zhou Dynasty.

CHAPTER
2

BUILDING VOCABULARY *Early River Valley Civilizations*

A. *Matching* Match the description in the second column with the term or name in the first column. Write the appropriate letter next to the word.

_____ 1. cultural diffusion

_____ 2. empire

_____ 3. polytheism

_____ 4. theocracy

_____ 5. hieroglyphics

_____ 6. papyrus

_____ 7. monsoon

_____ 8. loess

a. Egyptian writing system in which symbols stood for sounds as well as ideas

b. seasonal winds that dominate India's climate

c. group of peoples, nations, or previously independent states under the control of one ruler

d. paperlike writing surface that the Egyptians made from reeds

e. the belief in more than one god

f. fertile soil that forms a yellowish silt and is deposited when the Huang He overflows

g. process in which a new idea or a product spreads from one culture to another

h. type of government in which rule is based on religious authority

B. *Multiple Choice* Circle the letter before the term or name that best completes the sentence.

1. The Babylonian ruler who put together a single, uniform code of laws was (a) Narmer (b) Hammurabi (c) Herodotus.

2. An arc of land in Southwest Asia that provided rich farming land in ancient times is called the (a) Fertile Crescent (b) Harappan civilization (c) Mandate of Heaven.

3. A series of rulers from a single family is a (a) pharaoh (b) dynasty (c) theocracy.

4. The earliest civilization in Asia arose in (a) the Indus Valley (b) the Huang He Valley (c) Mesopotamia.

5. The Indus Valley civilization is also called the (a) Harappan civilization (b) Egyptian civilization (c) Shang dynasty.

6. The Chinese view that royal authority came from the gods is called the (a) dynastic cycle (b) feudalism (c) Mandate of Heaven.

C. *Writing* Write a paragraph describing how the ancient civilizations of Mesopotamia, Egypt, India, and China were governed using the following terms.

city-state   dynasty   pharaoh   feudalism

Name _____ Date _____

SKILLBUILDER PRACTICE *Interpreting Visual Sources*

Paintings, drawings, carved statues, and other visual sources are valuable clues to the past. Rich in detail, they reveal much about the historical period in which they were created. Look at the images on pages 42–43 of your textbook. Examine the different images of work and play in ancient Egypt and read the captions to learn more about the culture of Egypt. Then answer the questions that follow. (See Skillbuilder Handbook)

1. Look at the image of the temple. What types of craftsmen would be needed to complete this building?

_____

What type of organization would be needed to accomplish the building of this temple?

_____

_____

2. What do you think was painted on the walls and columns of the temple?

_____

_____

3. Look at the cosmetic box. What items are sitting on the top of the box? What did they contain?

_____

_____

4. What do you think the design on the side of the cosmetic box represents?

_____

_____

5. Study the senet game boards and the description of the game. What board games does it remind you of ? What might a modern player use to determine moves instead of sticks or knuckle bones?

_____

_____

CHAPTER 2

Section 2

GEOGRAPHY APPLICATION: HUMAN–ENVIRONMENT INTERACTION

Egypt and the Nile Delta

Directions: Read the paragraphs below and study the map carefully. Then answer the questions that follow.

A delta is a flat, triangular-shaped deposit of land found at the mouth of a river that empties into a normally still body of water. Deltas are formed when branches of a river carry soil downstream; the river's flow is slowed at the point of emptying, and soil is allowed to build up. Egypt's Nile River reaches its destination by first splitting into two main branches and then into numerous canals and streams, forming a delta out of an area that was once part of the Mediterranean Sea.

Egypt's famous Nile Delta is notable for more than being just the northern limit of the Nile River. The Delta is extremely fertile and thousands of years ago provided an environment for the formation of one of the world's first civilizations. The Nile Delta has long been considered an agricultural "fantasy"—containing more than one-half of Egypt's farmable land. Today the Delta is like a spider web of nearly 54,000 miles of canals. These canals provide water for the approximately 15 million Egyptians who live in the Delta's thousands of villages. The people grow everything from food and flowers, to cotton.

However, the Nile Delta region is not without some problems. In contrast to Upper Egypt of the south, with its more durable building stones, little of the Delta's ancient past survives. The Delta's structures were built primarily with mud bricks. As a result, today almost all of its ancient sites have been reduced to mere piles of mud. Also, drainage problems have arisen. Salts are coming to the surface and the Delta's fertility is declining. Pollution from untreated waste is increasing. In addition, the polar ice cap is slowly melting, causing the level of the Mediterranean Sea to rise. This process threatens to some day "drown" the Delta. Concrete dikes are now being built to try to hold back the Mediterranean.

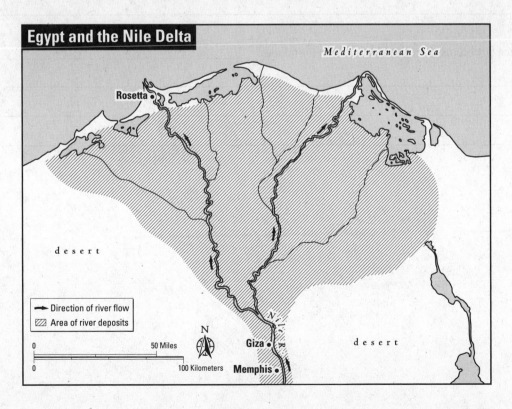

Egypt and the Nile Delta

Mediterranean Sea

Rosetta

→ Direction of river flow
▨ Area of river deposits

desert

N

0   50 Miles
0   100 Kilometers

Giza

Memphis

Nile R.

desert

Early River Valley Civilizations **27**

Interpreting Text and Visuals

1. Into what body of water does the Nile River empty? _____

2. In what direction does the Nile River flow? _____

3. The place where a river begins is known as its source. From Memphis, in which direction is the source of the Nile River? _____

4. How is the area of river deposits shown on the map? _____

5. What surrounds the Delta region? _____

_____

6. About how many miles long is the Delta's shoreline with the Mediterranean? _____

About how deep into the desert does the delta extend? _____

7. Describe the importance of the Nile Delta to Egypt. _____

_____

_____

_____

8. What problems does the Nile Delta region face? _____

_____

_____

_____

CHAPTER 2

Section 1

PRIMARY SOURCE Assyrian Letters

The following letters were etched on clay tablets in Akkadian, a language of ancient Mesopotamia. As you read, think about the worries and hopes of everyday life that each letter reflects.

A message from Ṣilla-Labbum and Elani:

Tell Puzur-Aššur, Amua, and Aššur-šamšī:

Thirty years ago you left the city of Assur. You have never made a deposit since, and we have not recovered one shekel of silver from you, but we have never made you feel bad about this. Our tablets have been going to you with caravan after caravan, but no report from you has ever come here. We have addressed claims to your father but we have not been claiming one shekel of your private silver. Please, do come back right away; should you be too busy with your business, deposit the silver for us. (Remember) we have never made you feel bad about this matter but we are now forced to appear, in your eyes, acting as gentlemen should not. Please, do come back right away or deposit the silver for us.

If not, we will send you a notice from the local ruler and the police, and thus put you to shame in the assembly of the merchants. You will also cease to be one of us.

Tell the Lady Zinû:

Iddin-Sin sends the following message:
May the gods Šamaš, Marduk, and Ilabrat keep you forever in good health for my sake.

From year to year, the clothes of the (young) gentlemen here become better, but you let my clothes get worse from year to year. Indeed, you persisted[?] in making my clothes poorer and more scanty. At a time when in our house wool is used up like bread, you have made me poor clothes. The son of Adad-iddinam, whose father is only an assistant of my father, (has) two new sets of clothes [*break*] while you fuss even about a single set of clothes for me. In spite of the fact that you bore me and his mother only adopted him, his mother loves him, while you, you do not love me!

from A. Leo Oppenheim, trans., *Letters from Mesopotamia,* (Chicago: University of Chicago Press, 1967), 76–77, 84–85.

Discussion Questions

1. *Determining Main Ideas* What is the merchants' complaint in the first letter?
2. *Clarifying* What will the debtors' punishment be if they fail to pay the debt?
3. *Drawing Conclusions* What is the complaint of Iddin-Sin to his mother in the second letter?
4. *Comparing and Contrasting* How would you compare the mood of the two letter writers?
5. *Drawing Conclusions* Based on your reading of these letters, what conclusions can you draw about everyday life in ancient Mesopotamia?

CHAPTER 2

Section 1

PRIMARY SOURCE *from* **The Code of Hammurabi**

More than 3,500 years ago, Hammurabi, king of the Babylonian Empire, ordered scribes to chisel a code of 282 laws onto a tall column of black stone. The column also featured an introduction explaining the intent of the code and a summary of Hammurabi's kingly deeds. As you read these laws from the code, think about how Mesopotamians defined crimes and how criminals were punished.

Before this portrait let every man who has a legal dispute come forward, read this text, and heed its precious words. The stone tablet will enlighten him in his trouble, and thus may he find justice and breathe easier in his heart, speaking these words: "Hammurabi is a king who cares for his people like a loving father."

1

If a man bring an accusation against a man, and charge him with a capital crime, but cannot prove it, he, the accuser, shall be put to death.

48

If a man owe a debt and Adad inundate his field and carry away the produce, or, through lack of water, grain have not grown in the field, in that year he shall not make any return of grain to the creditor, he shall alter his contract-tablet and he shall not pay the interest for that entire year.

53

If a man neglect to strengthen his dike and do not strengthen it, and a break be made in his dike and the water carry away the farm-land, the man in whose dike the break has been made shall restore the grain which he has damaged.

54

If he be not able to restore the grain, they shall sell him and his goods, and the farmers whose grain the water has carried away shall share the results of the sale.

113

If a man hold a debt of grain or money against a man, and if he take grain without the consent of the owner from the heap or the granary, they shall call that man to account for taking grain without the consent of the owner from the heap or the granary, and he shall return as much grain as he took, and he shall forfeit all that he has lent, whatever it be.

148

If a man take a wife and she become afflicted with disease, and if he set his face to take another, he may. His wife, who is afflicted with disease, he shall not put away. She shall remain in the house which he has built and he shall maintain her as long as she lives.

149

If that woman do not elect to remain in her husband's house, he shall make good to her the dowry which she brought from her father's house and she may go.

153

If a woman bring about the death of her husband for the sake of another man, they shall impale her.

195

If a son strike his father, they shall cut off his fingers.

196

If a man destroy the eye of another man, they shall destroy his eye.

197

If one break a man's bone, they shall break his bone.

200

If a man knock out a tooth of a man of his own rank, they shall knock out his tooth.

216

If he be a freeman, he (the physician) shall receive five shekels.

218

If a physician operate on a man for a severe wound with a bronze lancet [surgical knife] and cause the man's death; or open an abscess (in the eye) of a man with a bronze lancet and destroy the man's eye, they shall cut off his fingers.

225

    If he operate on an ox or a donkey for a severe wound and cause its death, he shall give the owner of the ox or donkey one fourth its value.

229

    If a builder build a house for a man and do not make its construction firm, and the house which he has built collapse and cause the death of the owner of the house, that builder shall be put to death.

250

    If a bull, when passing through the street, gore a man and bring about his death, this case has no penalty.

    I, Hammurabi, who was a perfect king to the downtrodden people entrusted to me by the god Enlil, I who was, by Marduk's order, their shepherd, have never tarried, never rested. I gave the people beautiful places, kept all pressing needs far away, and made their lives easier. With the mighty weapons given me by the gods Zababa and Ishtar, with the wisdom granted me by Ea, with the powers I hold from Marduk, I wiped out enemies on every side, put an end to wars, brought prosperity to our land, allowed men to live in peace and let no one fall upon them or harass them. I was called by the great gods, wherefore I became the good shepherd whose staff is straight. My righteous shadow has stretched across my city, I have gathered Sumer and Akkada in my arms, that they might thrive under my protection. I shield them in my peace and protect them in my wisdom. That the strong might not oppress the weak, that the widow and orphan might receive their due, here in Babylon . . . have I inscribed my precious words on a memorial stone and erected my statue as King of Justice.

from Robert Francis Harper, *The Code of Hammurabi, King of Babylon* (Chicago: The University of Chicago Press, 1904). Reprinted in Pierre Schwob, ed., *Great Documents of the World: Milestones of Human Thought* (Maidenhead, England: McGraw Hill, 1977).

Activity Options

1. ***Developing Historical Perspective*** With a small group, role-play Mesopotamians who live in the Babylonian Empire. Take turns acting as criminals who break specific laws in Hammurabi's Code, scribes who record the legal proceedings, and judges who sentence the criminals according to the code.

2. ***Comparing and Contrasting*** Invite a local attorney to speak to the class about today's judicial system. Discuss ways in which laws and penalties for breaking the law in the United States are similar and different to laws and penalties in the Babylonian Empire.

CHAPTER 2

Section 2

PRIMARY SOURCE Sphinx of Amenemhet III

Shown below, this statue of a sphinx—a mythological creature having the body of a lion and the head of a man, ram, or hawk—is made of black granite. It represents Amenemhet III, a pharaoh who ruled in the Twelfth Dynasty of the Middle Kingdom. What does this statue tell you about Egyptian culture?

Bildarchiv Foto Marburg.

Discussion Questions

1. *Categorizing* Imagine that you are a museum tour guide. What are some of this statue's distinguishing features that you might point out to a tour group? List at least three specific characteristics and share your list with classmates.

2. *Making Inferences* What can you learn about Egyptian culture from studying this statue?

3. *Comparing and Contrasting* Compare the Sphinx of Amenemhet III to a statue honoring an important person in today's society. How are these monuments similar? How are they different?

LITERATURE SELECTION Ancient Proverbs

Proverbs are wise sayings that express a basic truth. Archaeologists have discovered and translated thousands of proverbs from Mesopotamia, including those that follow. What do these proverbs reveal about Mesopotamian values and attitudes?

Proverbs from Mesopotamia

Translated by Robert H. Pfeiffer

1. Deal not badly with a matter, then no sorrow will fall into your heart.
2. Do no evil, then you will not clutch a lasting sorrow.
3. Do you strike the face of a walking ox with a strap?
4. The life of the day before yesterday is that of any day.
5. If the shoot is not right it will not produce the stalk, nor create seed.
6. Will ripe grain grow? How do we know? Will dried grain grow? How do we know?
7. Very soon he will be dead; (so he says), "Let me eat up (all I have)!" Soon he will be well; (so he says), "Let me economize!"
8. You go and take the field of the enemy; the enemy comes and takes your field.

Proverbs from Sumer

Translated by Edmund I. Gordon

1. A perverse child—his mother should never have given birth to him; his (personal) god should never have fashioned him!
2. The fox had a stick with him: "Whom shall I hit?" He carried a legal document with him: "What can I challenge?"
3. As long as he is alive, he is his friend; on the day of (his) death, he is his greatest adversary!
4. He could not bring about an agreement; the women were all talking to one another!
5. Into an open mouth, a fly will enter!
6. The horse, after he had thrown off his rider, said: "If my burden is always to be this, I shall become weak!"
7. The dog understands "Take it!" He does not understand "Put it down!"

from James B. Pritchard, ed., *The Ancient Near East, Vol. I* (Princeton, New Jersey: Princeton University Press, 1958), 244–245.

Discussion Questions

1. *Forming and Supporting Opinions* Which is your favorite proverb? Explain your answer.
2. *Making Inferences* What values are expressed by the first two proverbs?

3. *Drawing Conclusions* Do you think that these proverbs create a flattering portrait of Mesopotamian life? Why or why not?

LITERATURE SELECTION *from* **The Epic of Gilgamesh**

Archaeologists excavated 12 cuneiform tablets containing the story of Gilgamesh, a cruel and powerful king in ancient Sumer. One of the world's oldest epics, this poem centers around Gilgamesh's heroic yet fruitless quest to achieve immortality. In this excerpt from Tablet XI, Per-napishtim, a man who was granted immortality because he saved humankind from a great flood, explains to Gilgamesh how he prepared for the deluge brought about by angry gods. As you read, think about the steps Per-napishtim takes in order to survive the flood.

All that was necessary I collected together.
On the fifth day I drew its design;
In its middle part its sides were ten gar high;
Ten gar also was the extent of its deck;
I added a front-roof to it and closed it in.
I built it in six stories,
thus making seven floors in all;
The interior of each I divided again into nine partitions.
Beaks for water within I cut out.
I selected a pole and added all that was necessary.
Three (variant, five) shar of pitch I smeared on its outside;
three shar of asphalt I used for the inside (so as to make it water-tight). . . .
The ship sank into water two thirds of its height.
With all that I possessed I filled it;
with all the silver I had I filled it;
with all the gold I had I filled it;
with living creatures of every kind I filled it.
Then I embarked also all my family and my relatives,
cattle of the field, beasts of the field, and the uprighteous people—all them I embarked.
A time had Shamash appointed, (namely):
'When the rulers of darkness send at eventide a destructive rain,
then enter into the ship and shut its door.'
This very sign came to pass, and
The rulers of darkness sent a destructive rain at eventide.
I saw the approach of the storm,
and I was afraid to witness the storm;
I entered the ship and shut the door.
I intrusted the guidance of the ship to Purur-bel, the boatman,
the great house, and the contents thereof.
As soon as early dawn appeared,
there rose up from the horizon a black cloud,
within which the weather god (Adad) thundered,
and Nabu and the king of the gods (Marduk) went before.
The destroyers passed across mountain and dale (literally, country).
Dibbara, the great, tore loose the anchor-cable (?).
There went Ninib and he caused the banks to overflow;
the Anunnaki lifted on high (their) torches,
and with the brightness thereof they illuminated the universe.
The storm brought on by Adad swept even up to the heavens,

and all light was turned into darkness. . . .
Six days and nights
The wind blew, and storm and tempest overwhelmed the country.
When the seventh day drew nigh the tempest, the storm, the battle
which they had waged like a great host began to moderate.
The sea quieted down; hurricane and storm ceased.
I looked out upon the sea and raised loud my voice,
But all mankind had turned back into clay.
Like the surrounding field had become the bed of the rivers.
I opened the air-hole and light fell upon my cheek.
Dumfounded I sank backward, and sat weeping,
while over my cheek flowed the tears.
I looked in every direction, and behold, all was sea.
Now, after twelve (days?) there rose (out of the water) a strip of land.
To Mount Nisir the ship drifted.
On Mount Nisir the boat stuck fast and it did not slip away.
The first day, the second day, Mount Nisir held the ship fast, and did not let it slip away.
The third day, the fourth day, Mount Nisir held the ship fast, and did not let it slip away.
The fifth day, the sixth day, Mount Nisir held the ship fast, and did not let it slip away.
When the seventh day drew nigh
I sent out a dove, and let her go.
The dove flew hither and thither,
but as there was no resting-place for her, she returned.
Then I sent out a swallow, and let her go.
The swallow flew hither and thither,
but as there was no resting-place for her she also returned.
Then I sent out a raven, and let her go.
The raven flew away and saw the abatement of the waters.
She settled down to feed, went away, and returned no more.
Then I let everything go out unto the four winds, and I offered a sacrifice.
I poured out a libation upon the peak of the mountain.
I placed the censers seven and seven,
and poured into them calamus, cedar-wood, and sweet-incense.
The gods smelt the savour;
yea, the gods smelt the sweet savour;
the gods gathered like flies around the sacrificer.

from Rossiter Johnson, ed., *Assyrian and Babylonian
Literature* (New York: D. Appleton and Company,
1901), 351–357. Reprinted in Peter N. Stearns, ed.,
Documents in World History, Vol. I (New York:
HarperCollins Publishers, 1988), 13–15.

Research Options

1. *Comparing and Contrasting* Compare Per-napishtim's account of the flood with the Biblical account of the flood in Genesis. How are the two accounts similar? How are they different?

2. *Creating Oral Presentations* Find out more about epics like this one. What are some of the characteristics of an epic? In what other cultures around the world are epics found? Share your findings and a list of epic titles with classmates.

CHAPTER
2
Section 1

HISTORYMAKERS Hammurabi

Conquering King and Giver of Justice

"The great gods have called me, and I am indeed the good shepherd who brings peace. . . . I have carried in my bosom the people of Sumer and Akkad. Thanks to my good fortune they have prospered. I have not ceased to administer them in peace. By my wisdom I have harbored them."—Hammurabi's Code

King Hammurabi of Babylon stands alone among rulers of his day as both a dispenser of justice and a conqueror. He united much of Mesopotamia under the rule of Babylon and also created a famous code of laws.

Hammurabi became king in 1792 B.C. At the time Babylon controlled only a small area—lands within about 50 miles of the city. Babylon was just one among many city-states. Hammurabi was determined to expand his power and build an empire in Mesopotamia. Most of his military efforts aimed at winning control of the Tigris and Euphrates rivers, which brought water to his people's crops.

The king began by forming an alliance with the king of Larsa, to the south. Together they defeated a group called the Elamites. After conquering two cities to the south, Hammurabi moved north and east. Two decades later, he turned on his former ally and conquered Larsa. This brought the cities of ancient Sumer into his rule. Then he turned north again and defeated Marsi and Assyria.

The empire did not last long after his death in 1750 B.C., but his work had a major impact on the region. Before Hammurabi, the center of Mesopotamian culture had been Sumer. After his rule, Babylon became the core of that culture.

Hammurabi's other great achievement was his code of laws, which was discovered in the early 1900s by a team of archaeologists at work on the ancient site of Susa, in modern Iran. They uncovered an eight-foot-high pillar of stone, or stele. The black stone was polished bright and engraved with ancient cuneiform writing. The stele included an image as well—a portrait of King Hammurabi receiving the code from Marduk, a principal god of Babylon.

The writing on the stele is divided into three parts. The first part describes Hammurabi's conquests. The last offers the king's thoughts on justice. Most of the writing, though, is Hammurabi's Code. It is divided into 282 articles, each of which addresses a particular action. Each article states a particular event first, then gives a legal judgment to fit the event. The first article shows the pattern: "If a man has brought an accusation of murder against another man, without providing proof: the accuser shall be put to death."

Jean Bottéro, who studies ancient Babylon, believes that the code is a record of Hammurabi's actions as a judge. Its purpose, he says, is to guide future kings in their own decisions. In the last part of the code, Hammurabi talks to those kings who will follow him. He tells them to "heed the words that I have written on this stele: that the monument may explain to [you] the way and the behavior to follow."

The code reveals much about the people of ancient Babylon. The articles are grouped into several sections, each of which deals with a common concern. The first five all have to do with lying and the next 20 with theft. Remaining topics include farm labor (25 articles), trade (24), and money and debts (15). The two largest sections cover wives and family (67) and the work of various professions (61). Hammurabi's Code does call for some harsh penalties—including the famous "eye for an eye." However, that penalty only applied when a person destroyed the eye of an aristocrat. If the victim was a common person or a slave, the penalty was only a fine. The code also reflects the fact that the society was led by men. Fathers dominated families and had complete control over their children until the children married. Much of the code, though, was less harsh than earlier laws. At the end of the text, the king declared his desire to "prevent the powerful from oppressing the weak [and] . . . give my land fair decisions."

Questions

1. ***Determining Main Ideas*** What were Hammurabi's two achievements?
2. ***Making Inferences*** Was Hammurabi concerned about public opinion? Explain your answer.
3. ***Forming and Supporting Opinions*** Would you say that Hammurabi was a just king? Why or why not?

HISTORYMAKERS Tutankhamen
The Boy King

"At first I could see nothing . . . but presently, as my eyes grew accustomed to the light, details of the room within emerged slowly from the mist, strange animals, statues, and gold—everywhere the glint of gold."—Howard Carter, recalling the discovery of Tutankhamen's tomb

Thrust into the mantle of power at the age of nine or ten, Tutankhamen reigned as pharaoh, or king, of Egypt for only ten years, before dying at the young age of 18. His most important action was to restore ancient Egyptian religion. He was seldom remembered except by scholars who specialized in Egyptian history—until November 26, 1922. That day, archaeologist Howard Carter and George Herbert, a British nobleman, uncovered the tomb of this boy king and found such vast riches that he became the most famous pharaoh of all.

Tutankhamen came to the throne in a difficult time in Egyptian history. His father had tried to radically change the land's religion. He moved the capital of the kingdom away from Memphis. He abandoned the sacred city of Thebes. He declared that the god Aten was the only god of Egypt, replacing all others. The pharaoh had even changed his own name to Akhenaten to honor the new god.

The changes plunged Egypt into chaos. The pharaoh paid little heed to running his kingdom, and the people suffered. Later, after his death, he was angrily called the "criminal of Akhetaten," the name of his new capital city.

Akhenaten died after 17 years of rule. Soon afterward, a new name appeared on the scene: Tutankhaten, the son of Akhenaten. He became king of a land in turmoil.

Records show that under the young king, Egypt launched attacks on Nubia to the south and on Asia to the east. However, the boy ruler probably did not lead these military actions. Two older figures—an official named Ay and the general Horemheb—may have guided the country during the young pharaoh's reign. Both ruled Egypt after his death.

The young king's main accomplishment was not military but religious. He put an end to his father's experiment with the new religion of Aten. He moved the religious center of the kingdom back to Thebes and restored worship of the ancient gods. Tutankhaten also worked to restore the temples

and other sacred buildings that had fallen to decay. He even changed his name to Tutankhamen to show his reverence for the old gods. Tradition and order returned to Egyptian society. Soon after, however, the boy king died.

Though Tutankhamen had an important impact on Egypt, his reign was obscure to most people until Carter and Herbert brought his tomb to light. The rulers of ancient Egypt built elaborate tombs to house their bodies after death. Some were pyramids of stone. Others were cut into rock in the famous Valley of the Kings. These tombs were filled with gold, jewels, and other treasures for the pharaoh to enjoy in the afterlife. Over the years, however, robbers entered these burial places and took most objects of value. Archaeologists had long hoped to find a tomb that was intact.

Carter and Herbert's find provided that chance. The entrance to Tutankhamen's tomb had been covered over by workers who built a later tomb. As a result, his burial place had lain forgotten—and full of dazzling riches—for thousands of years. One spectacular treasure was the death mask of the king, a beautiful piece of solid gold. And the tomb revealed a wealth of other objects: "beads, boxes, stools, chariots, bows, arrows, shoes, gloves, underwear, food . . . and much more besides." Today many of these objects are displayed in museums. They give not just archaeologists, but all people, an opportunity to observe the glory of ancient Egypt.

Questions

1. **Recognizing Effects** How had Akhenaten's rule affected Egypt?
2. **Drawing Conclusions** Why was it significant that Tutankhamen changed his name?
3. **Making Inferences** Not all the objects in Tutankhamen's tomb were made of gold or jewels. Why might archaeologists want to study shoes, boxes, or food?

Name _____ Date _____

CHAPTER 2
Section 4

CONNECTIONS ACROSS TIME AND CULTURES
*River Civilizations in the
Ancient World*

*As you have read in Chapters 1 and 2, human societies formed civilizations in
fertile river valleys. People in Mesopotamia, Egypt, South Asia, and China
depended on rivers to maintain their lives. These widely separated river
civilizations all faced similar challenges. Compare the river systems in various
civilizations by answering the questions below.*

1. Accurately predicting the yearly floods was one of the challenges civilizations faced.
   What other problems were caused by the yearly floods?

   _____

2. Describe several solutions early civilizations devised to meet the challenge of
   growing crops during times of drought and to determine ownership of flooded fields.

   _____

3. Irrigation canals had to be constantly tended because they could fill up with silt.
   A report on Mesopotamia stated, "Stoppage of canals by silt depopulated villages
   and cities more effectively than the slaughter of people by an invading army."
   What do you think this statement means? _____

   _____

4. Irrigation canals would often fill up with silt during times of war.
   Why do you think this would happen? _____

   _____

5. How did the environment of the Indus Valley river civilization differ from that
   of Mesopotamia and Egypt? What was the effect of this environmental difference?

   _____

6. What lessons do you think modern-day farm societies can learn from the
   experiences of the ancient river civilizations? _____

   _____

CHAPTER 2
Section 3

SCIENCE & TECHNOLOGY *Early Water Engineering*

In addition to developing water systems for plumbing, ancient peoples also designed ways to control water to improve agriculture. In the dry regions of the Middle East, effective irrigation techniques for farming were a crucial element in the survival and growth of cities.

Around 6000 B.C., people settling in Mesopotamia initially attempted to bring water to farmland by digging small ditches leading away from springs. However, the Sumerians were the first civilization to conduct large-scale irrigation in an organized fashion. About 3000 B.C., water from both the Tigris and Euphrates rivers was delivered by a systematically developed network of dams, reservoirs, and canals.

Early Sumerian irrigation consisted of farmers simply carrying water from a river to their plots. As farmers increased the size and number of their fields, they cut narrow slots in the natural dams that had formed along the banks of these rivers. This allowed farmers to divert water to their tracts of land. Farmers also collected water in small reservoirs that they had built. They then lifted it from these pools into shallow irrigation ditches with the shaduf, a bailing bucket mounted on a long counter-weighted pole. The shaduf is still used today in many parts of the Middle East.

Increased watering allowed more land to be cultivated, and irrigation ditches soon covered the fields near the main rivers. Later, organized gangs of workers dug long canals to channel water to fields several miles from the rivers.

Soon, nearly every piece of farmland had a canal or waterway along one side of it. Whole-field watering was accomplished by opening the wall of a canal and flooding the field. Irrigating in this manner was important for both growing food and enabling the Sumerian plowmen to work the soil. In addition to nourishing the crops, the water helped soften the ground that had been baked hard by the intense sun and heat in the region.

The first *Farmer's Almanac* was written in Sumer and gave farmers specific guidance as to the timing, size, and number of crop waterings throughout the year. This advanced system of crop

J. Allan Cash Ltd.

The person on the far left fills the bucket on the shaduf with water. That person then swings the weighted pole around to fill the irrigation ditches.

irrigation helped the Sumerians produce a significant surplus of food, which supported the growth of cities in Mesopotamia.

Questions

Recognizing Facts and Details

1. What were the various methods that Sumerian farmers used to water their fields?
2. What is a shaduf?
3. ***Drawing Conclusions*** Why was it important to always have a canal or waterway next to a field?

Name _____ Date _____

Determining Main Ideas

Choose the word that most accurately completes each sentence below. Write that word in the blank provided.

Fertile Crescent	Nile	Gilgamesh
Sargon	cuneiform	empire
flooding	Euphrates	drought
culture	Egypt	cultural diffusion
Persia	polytheism	Tigris
Hammurabi	Sumer	Mesopotamia
dynasty	civilization	

1. The arc of land that falls between the Persian Gulf and the Mediterranean Sea in Southwest Asia is called _____.

2. That region also became known as _____, which means "land between the rivers" in Greek.

3. The two rivers that frame this arc of land are the _____ and the _____.

4. _____ and _____ were environmental problems common to this region.

5. One of the first city-states in Mesopotamia was _____.

6. Advanced cities, specialized workers, complex institutions, record keeping, and improved technology are all characteristics of a _____.

7. A series of rulers from a single family is called a _____.

8. _____ is the process in which a new idea or a product spreads from one culture to another.

9. The Sumerians believed in more than one god, a belief known as _____.

10. An _____ brings together several peoples, nations, or previously independent states under the control of one ruler.

11. The Sumerians developed a system of writing known as _____.

12. _____'s code of laws for the Babylonian Empire is his most enduring legacy.

Name _____ Date _____

Summarizing

Complete the chart below by listing the impact of each geographical characteristic of Egypt shown.

GEOGRAPHICAL CHARACTERISTICS OF EGYPT	IMPACT
Nile River: Benefits	1.
Nile River: Problems	2.
Vast deserts on either side of the Nile River: Benefits	3.
Vast deserts on either side of the Nile River: Problems	4.

Determining Main Ideas

Write your answers in the blanks provided.

5. Ruled Egypt as god-kings: _____

6. The type of government in which rule is based on religious authority: _____

7. Building in which Egyptian rulers were buried: _____

8. Process by which rulers' bodies were preserved: _____

9. Egyptian writing system: _____

10. Used by Egyptians as a writing surface: _____

Name _____ Date _____

_____

Determining Main Ideas
The following questions deal with early Indus Valley civilizations. Answer them in the
space provided.

1. What term do geographers use to refer to the landmass that includes India, Pakistan, and Bangladesh?
   _____

2. What geographic barriers separate India from the rest of the continent? _____
   _____

3. What seasonal winds dominate India's climate? _____
   _____

4. What environmental challenges do these winds provide? _____
   _____

5. What is another term for Indus Valley civilization? How did it get that name? _____
   _____

6. What are some examples of the sophisticated city planning of the Indus Valley people?
   _____
   _____

7. Why has it been impossible for linguists to decipher the Harappan language? _____
   _____
   _____

8. List three characteristics of Harappan culture. _____
   _____
   _____

9. What items did Harappans trade with peoples in the region? _____
   _____

10. What is the probable cause of the end of Indus Valley culture? _____
    _____

CHAPTER
2
Section 4

RETEACHING ACTIVITY *River Dynasties in China*

Reading Comprehension

Find the name or term in the second column that best matches the description in the first column. (Note: for question 1, more than one letter will be used.) Then write the letter(s) of your answer in the blank.

_____ 1. The two major river systems in China that flow from the west to the Pacific Ocean

_____ 2. The yellowish fertile soil deposited along riverbanks

_____ 3. China's heartland, the center of its civilization

_____ 4. Name used for the *Homo erectus* skeleton found in northern China near Beijing

_____ 5. The first Chinese dynasty to leave written records

_____ 6. The name the Chinese used to describe their own country as the center of the civilized world

_____ 7. Animal remnants and tortoise shells used to submit questions to the gods

_____ 8. Basis for Chinese system of writing

_____ 9. Divine approval for a Chinese ruler

_____ 10. The pattern of rise, decline, and replacement of ruling families in China

_____ 11. A political system in which nobles, or lords, are granted the use of lands that legally belong to the king

_____ 12. Dynasty that brought improvements in technology and trade to China beginning around 1027 B.C.

A. North China Plain

B. Middle Kingdom

C. pictographs

D. Peking man

E. Han Dynasty

F. dynastic cycle

G. oracle bones

H. Huang He

I. feudalism

J. Shang Dynasty

K. Chang Jiang

L. Mandate of Heaven

M. Zhou

N. loess

CHAPTER 3
Section 1

GUIDED READING *The Indo-Europeans*

A. *Summarizing* As you read about the migration of Indo-European peoples, fill in the blanks in the following summary.

From about 1700 to 1200 B.C., waves of Indo-European nomads migrated from

their homelands in the (1) _____, the dry grasslands north of the Caucasus

Mountains. One group, the Hittites, settled in (2) _____, a rugged peninsula

in a region today called Turkey. They conquered (3) _____, the chief city in

the Tigris-Euphrates valley, signed a peace treaty with Egypt, and blended many of their

traditions with the more advanced Mesopotamian culture. With their superior two-wheeled

(4) _____ and their war weapons made of (5) _____, the Hittites

created an empire that dominated Southwest Asia for over 450 years.

About 1500 B.C., another Indo-European group, the (6) _____, entered India

through the mountain passes of the Hindu Kush. Unlike the people they conquered, they were

light skinned and had not developed a writing system. The invaders were divided into social

classes, later called (7) _____. Over time four major social classes developed, the

highest being the (8) _____, or priests, and the lowest, the (9) _____,

or laborers. Beginning around 1000 B.C., chiefs began to set up kingdoms in the Indian

subcontinent; the most important of these kingdoms was (10) _____.

Many modern languages trace their origins to languages spoken by the Indo-Europeans.

Among the Indo-European family of languages spoken in Europe and Asia today are

(11) _____ and (12) _____.

B. *Writing for a Specific Purpose* Identify and explain the significance of the
Vedas and the *Mahabharata* in Indian history.

Name _____   Date _____

CHAPTER
3

Section 2

GUIDED READING *Hinduism and Buddhism Develop*

A. *Comparing and Contrasting* As you read about Hinduism and Buddhism, take notes to fill in the comparison chart below.

	Hinduism	**Buddhism**
1. Founder/Origins		
2. Key beliefs		
3. Gods		
4. Sacred literature		
5. Effect on society		
6. Modern-day traditions		

B. *Clarifying* On the back of this paper, describe the religious traditions and beliefs of **Jainism**.

People and Ideas on the Move 45

CHAPTER
3
Section 3

GUIDED READING *Seafaring Traders*

A. *Drawing Conclusions* As you read about the Minoan and Phoenician civilizations, write notes to explain what each statement listed below suggests about these seafaring traders.

1. Minoan cities had no fortifications.	→
2. Archaeologists excavating the Minoan capital city found the remains of wall paintings, seals, and fine painted pottery.	→
3. Many works of Minoan art depict women as major goddesses and priestesses.	→
4. Minoans sacrificed bulls to their gods and enjoyed the sport of bull-leaping.	→
5. The Phoenicians were the first Mediterranean people to sail beyond the Straits of Gibraltar, possibly even around Africa by way of the Red Sea.	→
6. The Phoenicians worked in wood, metal, glass, and ivory and produced red-purple dye from snails in the waters off the city-states of Sidon and Tyre.	→
7. There are some similarities among Phoenician, Greek, and modern-day alphabets.	→

B. *Writing Expository Paragraphs* On the back of this paper, explain the importance of the **Aegean Sea, King Minos,** and **Knossos** to the Minoans.

Name _____ Date _____

A. *Following Chronological Order* As you read this section, take notes to answer the questions about the time line.

2000 B.C.	God commands Abraham to take his people to Canaan.	1. What sacred writings describe the early history of the Hebrews?
1650 B.C.	Descendants of Abraham move to Egypt.	2. How were the Hebrews treated in Egypt?
1300-1200 B.C.	Hebrews begin their "exodus" from Egypt.	3. Why is Moses an important figure in Jewish history?
1020 B.C.	Hebrews unite and form the kingdom of Israel.	4. What were the achievements of Saul and David?
962 B.C.	King David is succeeded by his son Solomon.	5. Why did King Solomon build a great temple in Jerusalem?
922 B.C.	Kingdom splits into two, Israel and Judah.	6. What were the reasons for the division?
722 B.C.	Assyrians conquer Israel.	
586 B.C.	Chaldeans attack Jerusalem and destroy Solomon's Temple.	7. Who was Nebuchadnezzar?
515 B.C.	Second Temple is completed.	8. What ruler allowed the Hebrews to return to Jerusalem?

B. *Writing for a Specific Purpose* On the back of this paper, explain the significance of **Palestine, the covenant,** and **monotheism** to Judaism and the Hebrew people.

CHAPTER 3

BUILDING VOCABULARY *People and Ideas on the Move*

A. *Matching* Match the description in the second column with the term or name in the first column. Write the appropriate letter next to the word.

_____ 1. migration

_____ 2. Aryans

_____ 3. Jainism

_____ 4. Siddhartha Gautama

_____ 5. Minoans

_____ 6. Phoenicians

_____ 7. Abraham

_____ 8. covenant

a. religion that teaches everything in the universe has a soul and should not be harmed

b. founder of Buddhism

c. mutual promise between God and the founder of the Hebrew people

d. movement of a people from one region to another

e. "father" of the Hebrew people

f. Indo-European people who migrated to the Indus River Valley of India

g. seafaring people who lived on Crete and spread their culture through trade

h. powerful traders along the Mediterranean who developed an alphabet

B. *Evaluating* Write *T* in the blank if the statement is true. If the statement is false, write *F* in the blank and then write the corrected statement on the line below.

_____ 1. Many modern languages of Europe, Southwest Asia, and South Asia come from the languages of the Indo-Europeans.

_____

_____ 2. In a caste system, people can easily move from one social class to another.

_____

_____ 3. Knossos was a Phoenican capital city that was the center of an advanced and peaceful culture.

_____

_____ 4. According to the Torah, Moses led the Hebrews out of slavery.

_____

_____ 5. The Hebrews were united under kings Saul, David, and Solomon in a kingdom called Judah.

_____

C. *Writing* Write a paragraph describing some of the beliefs of Hinduism, Buddhism, and Judaism using the following terms.

reincarnation   karma   enlightenment   nirvana   monotheism

Name _____ Date _____

SKILLBUILDER PRACTICE *Forming and Supporting Opinions*

As you read about people and events in history, you form opinions. To support these opinions, you can cite facts, visual evidence, quotes, and other types of information you have found. Use the information in the passage below to form an opinion about Minoan civilization. Fill in the chart by writing your opinion of Minoan society and listing details to support your opinion. (See Skillbuilder Handbook)

The Minoans were known throughout the Mediterranean world for their arts and crafts, especially their paintings and fine pottery. They also crafted tools and weapons from bronze.

Minoan paintings depict both men and women hunting from chariots and participating in royal and religious ceremonies. Women also engaged in the popular sport of bull-leaping. According to one historian, "Minoan society apparently permitted women considerable freedom and equality."

The Minoans became rich from overseas trade that extended as far south as Egypt and as far east as Syria. To keep records, they used various forms of writing, one of which was an early form of Greek. With their great wealth, the Minoans built sprawling palaces with large courtyards and a maze of paved corridors, hallways, rooms, and baths with indoor plumbing. Some palaces even housed storerooms, a theater, and work areas. Around the palaces clustered prosperous towns connected by good roads.

Opinion:
Supporting details:

CHAPTER 3

Section 4

GEOGRAPHY APPLICATION: LOCATION
Early Eastern Mediterranean Civilizations

Directions: Read the paragraphs below and study the map carefully. Then answer the questions that follow.

In the thousand-year period that followed the decline of the Sumerians around 2000 B.C., several important civilizations sprouted in the region of the eastern Mediterranean Sea. Some did not survive the period, but most had a lasting impact. The map below shows the area of greatest land occupation of five of these civilizations during the second century B.C. Hittites flourished from about 2000 B.C. to 1190 B.C. Minoans ruled Mediterranean trade from about 2000 B.C. to 1400

B.C. Phoenicians emerged as the Mediterranean's strongest trading civilization around 1100 B.C. and ruled the sea until 842 B.C. Philistines came to the region in the 1200s B.C. and clashed with the Hebrews until being vanquished around 1000 B.C. Hebrews fled Egypt and returned to the eastern Mediterranean around 1200 B.C. They expanded north and south and united into a powerful kingdom around 1020 B.C.

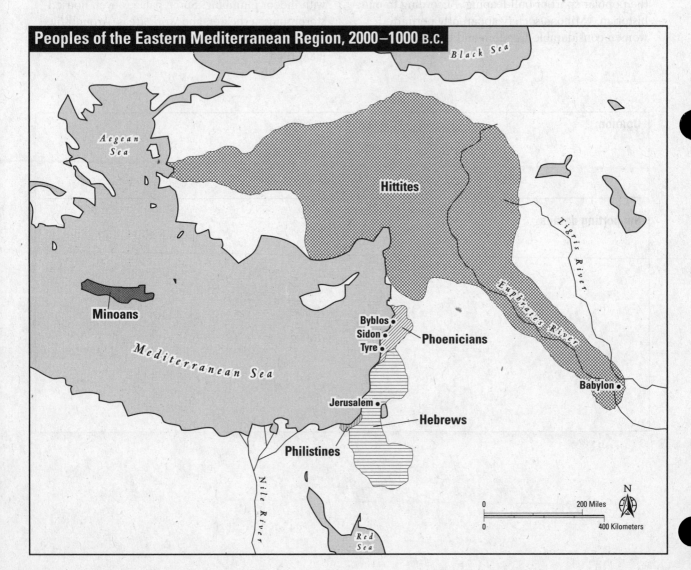

Peoples of the Eastern Mediterranean Region, 2000–1000 B.C.

Interpreting Text and Visuals

1. What are the five eastern Mediterranean civilizations covered on the map?_____

_____

2. Which eastern Mediterranean civilization ruled the largest territory during the millennium of
   2000 B.C. to 1000 B.C.? _____

Describe the extent of that territory. _____

_____

3. What major city-states are shown on the map? _____

_____

4. What unique situation made the Minoans dominant in Mediterranean trade from about 2000 B.C.
   to 1400 B.C.? _____

_____

5. Who succeeded the Minoans as the most powerful Mediterranean trader? _____

_____

Look at the map. Why is it no surprise that this civilization eventually came to dominate the
Mediterranean?_____

_____

6. Which eastern Mediterranean civilizations do you think caused the Hebrews the most problems?

_____

CHAPTER

3

Section 1

PRIMARY SOURCE *from the* Rig Veda

Written in Sanskrit, the Rig Veda *is the oldest of the four* Vedas, *India's earliest religious text. The* Rig Veda *consists of 1,028 hymns addressed to Aryan gods. Whom do the following hymns address?*

"To Dawn"

She hath shone brightly like a youthful woman,
   stirring to motion every living creature.
Agni hath come to feed on mortals' fuel. She hath
   made light and chased away the darkness.

Turned to this all, far-spreading, she hath risen and
   shone in brightness with white robes about her.
She hath beamed forth lovely with golden colours,
   mother of kine, guide of the days she bringeth.

Bearing the gods' own eye, auspicious lady, leading
   her courser white and fair to look on,
Distinguished by her beams, Dawn shines appar-
   ent, come forth to all the world with wondrous
   treasure.

Dawn nigh will wealth and dawn away the foeman:
   prepare for us wide pasture free from danger.
Drive away those who hate us, bring us riches:
   pour bounty, opulent lady, on the singer.

Send thy most excellent beams to shine and light
   us, giving us lengthened days, O Dawn, O goddess,
Granting us food, thou who hast all things precious, and bounty rich in chariots, kine, and
   horses.

O Dawn, nobly-born, daughter of heaven, whom
   the Vasisthas with their hymns make mighty,
Bestow thou on us vast and glorious riches.
   Preserve us evermore, ye gods, with blessings.

"To Night"

With all her eyes the goddess Night looks forth
   approaching many a spot:
She hath put all her glories on.

Immortal, she hath filled the waste, the goddess
   hath filled height and depth:
She conquers darkness with her light.

The goddess as she comes hath set the Dawn her
   sister in her place:
And then the darkness vanishes.

So favour us this night, O thou whose pathways we
   have visited
As birds their nest upon the tree.

The villagers have sought their homes, and all that
   walks and all that flies,
Even the falcons fain for prey.

Keep off the she-wolf and the wolf; O Night, keep
   the thief away:
Easy be thou for us to pass.

Clearly hath she come nigh to me who decks the
   dark with richest hues:
O morning, cancel it like debts.

These have I brought to thee like kine. O Night,
   thou child of heaven, accept
This laud as for a conqueror.

from Nicol Macnicol, trans., *The Rig Veda.* Reprinted in
Hinduism (New York: George Braziller, 1962), 63, 71.

Activity Options

1. ***Describing Character*** With classmates, take
turns reading these hymns aloud. Then discuss
your impressions. What did Aryans ask of each
goddess? Which lines best convey the traits and
qualities possessed by each goddess?
2. ***Using Visual Stimuli*** Draw a sketch of Dawn
based on your reading of the hymn.

Name _____ Date _____

CHAPTER 3

Section 1

PRIMARY SOURCE *from the* Bhagavad-Gita

The Bhagavad-Gita *is an ancient text of Hinduism whose title means "The Song of God." Part of the epic poem the* Mahabharata, *the* Bhagavad-Gita *takes the form of a dialogue about the meaning of life between the warrior Arjuna and his charioteer Krishna, who is really the god Vishnu in disguise. This excerpt occurs before a battle between forces loyal to Arjuna's older brother and those loyal to his cousin. As you read, think about Arjuna's response to war.*

Arjuna saw them standing there:
fathers, grandfathers, teachers,
uncles, brothers, sons,
grandsons, and friends.

He surveyed his elders
and companions in both armies,
all his kinsmen
assembled together.

Dejected, filled with strange pity,
he said this:

> "Krishna, I see my kinsmen
> gathered here, wanting war.

> My limbs sink,
> my mouth is parched,
> my body trembles,
> the hair bristles on my flesh. . . .

> I see omens of chaos,
> Krishna; I see no good
> in killing my kinsmen
> in battle. . . .

> They are teachers, fathers, sons,
> and grandfathers, uncles, grandsons,
> fathers and brothers of wives,
> and other men of our family.

> I do not want to kill them
> even if I am killed, Krishna;
> not for kingship of all three worlds,
> much less for the earth! . . .

> How can we ignore the wisdom
> of turning from this evil
> when we see the sin
> of family destruction, Krishna?

> When the family is ruined,
> the timeless laws of family duty
> perish; and when duty is lost,
> chaos overwhelms the family. . . .
> The sins of men who violate
> the family create disorder in society
> that undermines the constant laws
> of caste and family duty.

> Krishna, we have heard
> that a place in hell
> is reserved for men
> who undermine family duties.

> I lament the great sin
> we commit when our greed
> for kingship and pleasures
> drives us to kill our kinsmen.

> If Dhritarashtra's armed sons
> kill me in battle when I am unarmed
> and offer no resistance,
> it will be my reward."

Saying this in the time of war,
Arjuna slumped into the chariot
and laid down his bow and arrows,
his mind tormented by grief.

from Barbara Stoler Miller, trans., *The Bhagavad-Gita* (New York: Bantam, 1986), 24–27.

Discussion Questions
Determining Main Ideas
1. How does Arjuna feel just before the battle?
2. Why does Arjuna believe it is wrong to kill members of his family?
3. ***Making Inferences*** What values does this excerpt reflect?

PRIMARY SOURCE Dolphin Fresco from Knossos

The walls of the Minoan palace of Knossos were decorated with colorful paintings. Study this detail from one of the wall paintings. Why do you think Minoan artists might have chosen to paint dolphins and other sea creatures?

Copyright © R. Sheridan/Ancient Art & Architecture Collection.

Research Options

1. ***Analyzing Information*** The wall paintings at the palace of Knossos, including this one, are examples of frescoes. Find out more about frescoes and how they are created. Share your findings with the class.
2. ***Writing Informative Compositions*** Work with a small group of classmates to locate photographs of other Minoan wall paintings and other artifacts. Discuss the paintings and artifacts and draw conclusions about Minoan culture based on your observations. Then write a short report to present your group's conclusions.
3. ***Using Research in Writing*** Research the palace of Knossos. Then create a chart listing relevant facts such as how large it was, what it was used for, and who excavated its ruins.

CHAPTER 3

Section 4

PRIMARY SOURCE The Ten Commandments
from The New English Bible

According to the Bible, God revealed the Ten Commandments to the Hebrew leader Moses at Mount Sinai. These commandments, which have been preserved in the Old Testament in Exodus 20: 1–17 and Deuteronomy 5: 6–21, established a code of ethical conduct that became the basis for the civil and religious laws of Judaism. How should people behave responsibly, according to the Ten Commandments?

The Lord came down upon the top of Mount Sinai and summoned Moses to the mountaintop, and Moses went up. The Lord said to Moses, "Go down; warn the people solemnly that they must not force their way through to the Lord to see him, or many of them will perish. Even the priests, who have access to the Lord, must hallow themselves, for fear that the Lord may break out against them." Moses answered the Lord, "The people cannot come up Mount Sinai, because thou thyself didst solemnly warn us to set a barrier to the mountain and so to keep it holy." The Lord therefore said to him, "Go down; then come up and bring Aaron with you, but let neither priests nor people force their way up to the Lord, for fear that he may break out against them." So Moses went down to the people and spoke to them.

God spoke, and these were his words:

I am the Lord your God who brought you out of Egypt, out of the land of slavery.

You shall have no other god to set against me.

You shall not make a carved image for yourself nor the likeness of anything in the heavens above, or on the earth below, or in the waters under the earth. You shall not bow down to them or worship them; for I, the Lord your God, am a jealous god. I punish the children for the sins of the fathers to the third and fourth generations of those who hate me. But I keep faith with thousands, with those who love me and keep my commandments.

You shall not make wrong use of the name of the Lord your God; the Lord will not leave unpunished the man who misuses his name.

Remember to keep the Sabbath day holy. You have six days to labour and do all your work. But the seventh day is a Sabbath of the Lord your God; that day you shall not do any work, you, your son or your daughter, your slave or your slave-girl, your cattle or the alien within your gates; for in six days the Lord made heaven and earth, the sea, and all

that is in them, and on the seventh day he rested. Therefore the Lord blessed the Sabbath day and declared it holy.

Honour your father and your mother, that you may live long in the land which the Lord your God is giving you.

You shall not commit murder.

You shall not commit adultery.

You shall not steal.

You shall not give false evidence against your neighbour.

You shall not covet your neighbour's house; you shall not covet your neighbour's wife, his slave, his slave-girl, his ox, his [donkey], or anything that belongs to him.

When all the people saw how it thundered and the lightning flashed, when they heard the trumpet sound and saw the mountain smoking, they trembled and stood at a distance. "Speak to us yourself," they said to Moses, "and we will listen; but if God speaks to us we shall die." Moses answered, "Do not be afraid. God has come only to test you, so that the fear of him may remain with you and keep you from sin."

from The New English Bible (Cambridge University Press, 1970), 81–87. Reprinted in Peter N. Stearns, ed., *Documents in World History, vol. 1* (New York: HarperCollins, 1988), 26–27.

Discussion Questions

Determining Main Ideas

1. According to these laws, how should the Hebrew people act toward the Lord?
2. How should the Hebrews act toward others?
3. ***Comparing and Contrasting*** How do the religious teachings represented in the Ten Commandments differ from the religious beliefs reflected by the hymns you read from the *Rig Veda*?

CHAPTER 3
Section 2

LITERATURE SELECTION *from the* **Ramayana**
by Valmiki

The **Ramayana** *is a Sanskrit epic about the classic struggle between good and evil. In this prose retelling of a passage from the* **Ramayana,** *the Hindu god Vishnu in the form of Prince Rama battles Ravana, the Demon King, with the help of Indra, the rain god, and Indra's charioteer Matali. Who wins the battle?*

Rama and Ravana dueled with arrows. One after another, Rama broke the bows out of Ravana's hands until ninety-nine were gone and only one remained. The Demon King shot arrows long and short, thick and thin, quick and slow, from close range or far away; but Rama's armor was hard and impenetrable, he was unharmed and many arrows melted away when he saw them come.

Ravana seized his mace of iron set with lapis stones and embellished with gold, hung with iron-mouthed bells and entwined with red blossoms, for years daily washed with blood and now smoking and straining to strike, an eight-sided mace which would return from flight into the thrower's hands. Ravana drove to attack. He gripped the iron handle with four hands and swung as the chariots met. It was too soon and the blow fell on the charioteer and not Rama, but Matali knocked that mace hard aside with his bronze fist.

Then Ravana drew apart and stopped. He whirled his mace in a circle rising and dipping his heads; and the mace moaned—Woe . . . Woe . . . Woe— The mace went faster and faster. Matali drove to deceive Ravana's aim and Rama reached for Indra's weapons-racks. He took a spear, held it in one hand, slapped it with the palm of his other hand and threw it. That great dart went at Ravana reso-nant and vibrating with sound, with a noise like the thunder of a rockslide, a loud falling noise like a cliff falling, the dark world falling, Ravana falling . . . Rama opened a long bamboo case at his belt and

took out the brass-bladed grass arrow given to him by Agastya, and notched it on his bowstring. That arrow could rend walls and gateways of stone; it breathed and sighed. Rama pulled his bow. He took three aiming steps backwards and held his breath. . . .

Rama shot. The bowstring rang out, all over the Universe. That arrow first broke the sword and bow Ravana raised to ward it, then it hit Ravana's breast and struck through his heart, stealing his life, and never stopped, but came out from his back and entered the Earth.

Down from Ravana's hands fell his broken bow and sword, and the Demon King of Lanka fell dying in his own dark form.

from William Buck, trans., *Ramayana* (New York: New American Library, 1976), 281–284.

Activity Options

1. *Analyzing Information* Draw a comic strip based on the battle between Prince Rama and Ravana. Post your work on a classroom bulletin board.

2. *Writing Descriptive Paragraphs* Write a newspaper report about the encounter between Prince Rama and Ravana. Include a catchy head-line.

3. *Summarizing Written Texts* Compose a song about the heroic contest fought in this excerpt.

CHAPTER 3

Section 2

LITERATURE SELECTION *from Siddhartha*
by Herman Hesse
Translated by Hilda Rasner

In his novel **Siddhartha,** *the 20th-century German author Hermann Hesse recreates the life of Siddhartha Gautama, the founder of Buddhism, in fictional form. As you read this excerpt from the novel, think about how Siddhartha feels before and after his awakening.*

Awakening

As Siddhartha left the grove in which the Buddha, the Perfect One, remained, in which Govinda remained, he felt that he had also left his former life behind him in the grove. As he slowly went on his way, his head was full of this thought. He reflected deeply, until this feeling completely overwhelmed him and he reached a point where he recognized causes; for to recognize causes, it seemed to him, is to think, and through thought alone feelings become knowledge and are not lost, but become real and begin to mature.

Siddhartha reflected deeply as he went on his way. He realized that he was no longer a youth; he was now a man. He realized that something had left him, like the old skin that a snake sheds. Something was no longer in him, something that had accompanied him right through his youth and was part of him: this was the desire to have teachers and to listen to their teachings. He had left the last teacher he had met, even he, the greatest and wisest teacher, the holiest, the Buddha. He had to leave him; he could not accept his teachings.

Slowly the thinker went on his way and asked himself: What is it that you wanted to learn from teachings and teachers, and although they taught you much, what was it they could not teach you? And he thought: It was the Self, the character and nature of which I wished to learn. I wanted to rid myself of the Self, to conquer it, but I could not conquer it, I could only deceive it, could only fly from it, could only hide from it. Truly, nothing in the world has occupied my thoughts as much as the Self, this riddle, that I live, that I am one and am separated and different from everybody else, that I am Siddhartha; and about nothing in the world do I know less than about myself, about Siddhartha. The thinker, slowly going on his way, suddenly stood still, gripped by this thought, and another

thought immediately arose from this one. It was: The reason why I do not know anything about myself, the reason why Siddhartha has remained alien and unknown to myself is due to one thing, to one single thing—I was afraid of myself, I was fleeing from myself. I was seeking Brahman, Atman, I wished to destroy myself, to get away from myself, in order to find in the unknown innermost, the nucleus of all things, Atman, Life, the Divine, the Absolute. But by doing so, I lost myself on the way. Siddhartha looked up and around him, a smile crept over his face, and a strong feeling of awakening from a long dream spread right through his being. Immediately he walked on again, quickly, like a man who knows what he has to do.

Yes, he thought, breathing deeply, I will no longer try to escape from Siddhartha. I will no longer devote my thoughts to Atman and the sorrows of the world. I will no longer mutilate and destroy myself in order to find a secret behind the ruins. I will no longer study Yoga-Veda, Atharva-Veda, or asceticism, or any other teachings. I will learn from myself, be my own pupil; I will learn from myself the secret of Siddhartha.

He looked around him as if seeing the world for the first time. The world was beautiful, strange and mysterious. Here was blue, here was yellow, here was green, sky and river, woods and mountains, all beautiful, all mysterious and enchanting, and in the midst of it, he, Siddhartha, the awakened one, on the way to himself. All this, all this yellow and blue, river and wood, passed for the first time across Siddhartha's eyes. It was no longer the magic of Mara, it was no more the veil of Maya, it was no longer meaningless and the chance diversities of the appearances of the world, despised by deep-thinking Brahmins, who scorned diversity, who sought unity. River was river, and if the One and Divine in Siddhartha secretly lived in blue and river, it was just the divine art and intention that there should be yellow and blue, there sky and wood—and here Siddhartha. Meaning and reality were not hidden somewhere behind things, they were in them, in all of them.

How deaf and stupid I have been, he thought, walking on quickly. When anyone reads anything which he wishes to study, he does not despise the letters and punctuation marks, and call them illusion, chance and worthless shells, but he reads them, he studies and loves them, letter by letter. But I, who wished to read the book of the world and the book of my own nature, did presume to despise the letters and signs. I called the world of appearances, illusion. I called my eyes and tongue, chance. Now it is over; I have awakened. I have indeed awakened and have only been born today.

But as these thoughts passed through Siddhartha's mind, he suddenly stood still, as if a snake lay in his path.

Then suddenly this also was clear to him: he, who was in fact like one who had awakened or was newly born, must begin his life completely afresh. When he left the Jetavana grove that morning, the grove of the Illustrious One, already awakened, already on the way to himself, it was his intention and it seemed the natural course for him after the years of his asceticism to return to his home and his father. Now, however, in that moment as he stood still, as if a snake lay in his path, this thought also came to him: I am no longer what I was, I am no longer an ascetic, no longer a priest, no longer a Brahmin. What then shall I do at home with my father? Study? Offer sacrifices? Practice meditation? All this is over for me now.

Siddhartha stood still and for a moment an icy chill stole over him. He shivered inwardly like a small animal, like a bird or a hare, when he realized how alone he was. He had been homeless for years and had not felt like this. Now he did feel it. Previously, when in deepest meditation, he was still his father's son, he was a Brahmin of high standing, a religious man. Now he was only Siddhartha, the awakened; otherwise nothing else. He breathed in deeply and for a moment he shuddered. Nobody was so alone as he. He was no nobleman, belonging to any aristocracy, no artisan belonging to any guild and finding refuge in it, sharing its life and language. He was no Brahmin, sharing the life of the Brahmins, no ascetic belonging to the Samanas. Even the most secluded hermit in the woods was not one and alone; he also belonged to a class of people. Govinda had become a monk and thousands of monks were his brothers, wore the same gown, shared his beliefs and spoke his language. But he, Siddhartha, where did he belong? Whose life would he share? Whose language would he speak?

At that moment, when the world around him melted away, when he stood alone like a star in the heavens, he was overwhelmed by a feeling of icy despair, but he was more firmly himself than ever. That was the last shudder of his awakening, the last pains of birth. Immediately he moved on again and began to walk quickly and impatiently, no longer homewards, no longer to his father, no longer looking backwards.

Discussion Questions

Determining Main Ideas

1. How does Siddhartha feel before his awakening?
2. How does he feel after his awakening?
3. ***Drawing Conclusions*** What kind of person do you think Siddhartha is, based on your reading of this excerpt?

HISTORYMAKERS Siddhartha Gautama
Enlightened One

"Let a man overcome anger by love, let him overcome evil by good. Let him overcome the greedy by liberality, the liar by truth."—Siddhartha Gautama, the Buddha

Born a prince in a warrior family, Siddhartha Gautama lived in northern India during a time of turmoil. From a young age, he was disturbed by the suffering of his world. Unsatisfied with the life of ease, he hoped to find deeper meaning in his life. He tried many ways of reaching inner peace, but none worked. When he finally discovered his path, he decided to teach others how to reach that same state—and in doing so, founded a new religion. Siddhartha was born near the foot of the Himalaya Mountains. His father ruled a small kingdom and hoped that his son would follow after him. Siddhartha was not the typical prince, however. He was concerned more with spiritual matters and wrestled with deep questions about human life. He asked himself, "Why is there suffering and what is death?" Hoping to settle his son down, the king built him a palace, but Siddhartha continued to be restless. At age 29, he later recalled, he broke with his comfortable life:

> In the days before my enlightenment . . . I bethought me that a hole-and-corner life is all that a home can give, whereas a wandering [religious man] is as free as air. . . . So the time came, when I was quite young and with a wealth of coal-black hair untouched by gray and in all the beauty of my early prime— despite the wishes of my parents, who wept and lamented—I cut off my hair and beard . . . and went off from home.

He tried for six years to find the solution to his spiritual longing. In the end meditation provided the answer. He experienced the Bodhi, or moment of enlightenment. Life is suffering, he decided, but people do not realize this fact and try to achieve pleasure. By following Siddhartha's eight rules or the Eightfold Path, one can end desire and bring about the needed understanding. Then the person experiences a release from suffering, a state called nirvana. Siddhartha came to be called the Buddha, or "Enlightened One." He quickly went to a park in the Indian city of Benares and preached his first

sermon. He continued for 46 years, traveling throughout India. Soon he had many followers. The Buddha had great compassion for people, and he strongly rejected the inequality that was a central part of India's caste system. In this system, the Brahmins, or priests, were considered the most worthy of people. The outcasts, or untouchables, were shunned by all others. People lived in the caste into which they were born. The Buddha once said, "Not by birth does one become an outcast, not by birth does one become a Brahmin. By deeds one becomes an outcast, by deeds one becomes a Brahmin." He was reinforcing the message made clear in another saying: "Hatred does not cease by hatred at any time; hatred ceases by love."

The Buddha gathered large numbers of followers. He did not want to create a religion that relied on a strict hierarchy to grow. He once told his followers, "Be ye lamps unto yourselves. Be a refuge to yourselves. Hold fast to the truth as to a lamp. Look not for refuge to anyone besides yourselves."

Even in his death, the Buddha showed his feeling for others. As the story goes, the Buddha was 80 years old when he took a meal offered by a poor believer. The food was spoiled, but the Buddha did not wish to hurt the feelings of his host and ate it anyway—although he prevented his followers from joining him. Soon after, he was taken sick. He laid down in a grove of trees and gave his final instructions to his followers. As he lay dying, he sent a messenger to the poor man who had cooked the fatal meal to reassure the man that he should not feel any blame. Soon after, he died. According to Buddhist belief, his soul passed into nirvana.

Questions

1. *Drawing Conclusions* Explain what you think the Buddha means by the quote on this page.
2. *Formng and Supporting Opinions* Do you agree with the Buddha's idea that all life is suffering? Explain.
3. *Hypothesizing* How could the Buddha's message about the caste system undermine Hindu society?

CHAPTER
3
Section 3

HISTORYMAKERS Herodotus
Father of History

"This is the demonstration of the research of Herodotus of Halicarnassus."
—Herodotus, opening line of the Histories

Herodotus was one of the first people to try to explain the past. For this, he became known as the "father of history." Many historians have been uncomfortable about that label, because the history written by Herodotus has many flaws. Nevertheless, with his *Histories*, Herodotus created a new form of study. Indeed, the name of this field—history—was coined by him. In his native Greek, it means "inquiries" or "research."
Not much is known about the life of this first historian. He was born about 484 B.C. in Halicarnassus, a city in Asia Minor that was settled by Greeks. His family was well-off but suffered at the hands of the tyrant who ran the government of that city. They were forced to leave for an island while Herodotus was still young. Later in life, he returned to his home to help overthrow the tyrant, but he did not stay.
Herodotus has been described as curious. One later writer called him "a man who could not cross the street without finding something interesting." He traveled a great deal throughout the area, going as far as the Black Sea, Syria, Babylon, Palestine, and Egypt. The reason for this travel is unknown. He may have been engaged in trade, a common enough pursuit for Greeks of his time. Whatever the reason, he constantly asked questions of the people he met. In this way he gained understanding of the customs and traditions of people in other lands. About 450, he went to live in Athens, where he became close friends with the famous playwright Sophocles. Later, he moved to a Greek colony in southern Italy. He lived there until the end of his life, which was some time around 420 B.C.
Scholars are unsure when Herodotus began writing his history, how long it took, or in what order the parts were written. It is clear that he was already at work on it when he lived in Athens. There are reports that he read parts of it aloud while he lived in that city.
Herodotus' main purpose was to tell the story of the conflict between Persia and the Greek city-states in the early years of the fifth century B.C. His book describes the Persian invasions and the Greeks' unexpected victory. The first third relates the rise of Persia. The middle third details the beginning of the Persian-Greek conflict up to the Battle of Marathon. The last third chronicles the massive invasion launched by Persian leader Xerxes in 480–479 and the ultimate Persian defeat. The work includes much more, however. Herodotus presents a great deal of background information on the roots of Persian and Greek society before the two peoples ever clashed. In addition, the portion called Book Two is a long and detailed passage about Egypt. It includes accounts of Egyptian history as well as his observations of life and customs in that land.
To many historians, though, Herodotus' book is frustrating. He pays little attention to chronology—the sequence of events over time. He also includes many stories that bring in unbelievable elements, including the actions of the gods.
With these problems, what makes the work a history? First, Herodotus keeps his eye on the story that he wants to tell. Despite wandering off to cover side topics, he still conveys the main events. Second, he tells his story with some objectivity. He is able to distance himself from the persons whose actions he describes and comment on them in a fair way. Third, although he was, for the most part, a poor judge of sources, he did attempt to assess their reliability. Fourth, he does try to offer insights about the causes and effects of events, even though his analysis is somewhat naive and superficial. Finally, he accomplishes all these goals with a graceful and charming writing style.

Questions

1. *Making Inferences* Why do you think Herodotus would call his work "researches" or "inquiries"?
2. *Analyzing Motives* If Herodotus was a Greek, was it possible for him to be completely objective in his history? Explain.
3. *Developing Historical Perspective* What do you think are the characteristics that make a piece of writing a history?

Name _____ Date _____

CHAPTER 3

Section 4

CONNECTIONS ACROSS TIME AND CULTURES
Religions in the Ancient World

THEMATIC CONNECTION:
RELIGIOUS AND ETHICAL SYSTEMS

Since ancient times, religion has greatly affected how people live, the governments they form, and the way they view the world. In this chapter you have read about the origins of Hinduism, Buddhism, and Judaism. Compare these religions with the religions of ancient Sumer and Egypt by answering the following questions.

1. The ancient civilizations of Egypt and Sumer worshiped many gods. How do their polytheistic beliefs compare with those of ancient

    Hinduism? _____

    Buddhism? _____

    Judaism? _____

2. Sumerians worshiped their gods from the Ziggurat, the largest building in the city. Ancient Egyptians built temples to worship their gods and pyramids as homes for their god-kings. How did the ancient Hebrews maintain their religion as they traveled from place to place? _____

    _____

3. In Sumer the king was a representative of the gods. In Egypt the king was worshiped as a god. What role did the kings play in religion in ancient Israel? _____

    _____

4. Sumerians made offerings of animals, grain, fabric, and jewels in order to please their gods. What did ancient Hebrews need to do to please their God? _____

    _____

5. Sumerians saw the afterlife as a dismal, joyless place. Ancient Egyptians anticipated a pleasant life after they died. What vision of life after death did Hinduism and Buddhism share? _____

    _____

Name _____ Date _____

Making Inferences

Below are some general statements about the Indo-European migration into Europe.
Read each statement. Then supply details from the section to support it.

1. The Indo-Europeans were a group of nomadic peoples who came from the region north of the Caucasus.

    a. _____
    b. _____

2. The Indo-European family of languages were the ancestors of many of the modern languages of

    Europe, Southwest Asia, and South Asia.

    a. _____
    b. _____

3. One group of Indo-European speakers were the Hittites.

    a. _____
    b. _____

4. The Hittites brought greatly improved technology for warfare.

    a. _____
    b. _____

5. Around 1500 B.C., another Indo-European people, the Aryans, moved into the Indus River Valley of India.

    a. _____
    b. _____

6. The Aryans were different from the *dasas*, the people they found in India.

    a. _____
    b. _____

7. When they first came to India, the Aryans were divided into three social classes.

    a. _____
    b. _____

8. Eventually, the Aryan class structure became a caste system.

    a. _____
    b. _____

Name _____ Date _____

RETEACHING ACTIVITY *Hinduism and Buddhism Develop*

Comparing and Contrasting

Complete the chart below by recording details to compare and contrast the development of Hinduism and Buddhism.

	HINDUISM	**BUDDHISM**
Origin/founder	1.	2.
Who believers worship	3.	4.
Leaders	5.	6.
Sacred texts	7.	8.
Basic beliefs	9.	10.
	11.	12.
	13.	14.
Attitude toward caste system	15.	16.

CHAPTER
3
Section 3

RETEACHING ACTIVITY *Seafaring Traders*

Multiple Choice
Choose the best answer for each item. Write the letter of your answer in the blank.

____1. A powerful seafaring people who dominat-
ed trade in the eastern Mediterranean
from about 2000 to 1400 B.C. were the
   a. Romans.
   b. Minoans.
   c. Aryans.
   d. Mesopotamians.

____2. The capital city of these people was
   a. Knossos.
   b. Phoenicia.
   c. Crete.
   d. Byblos.

____3. Bull-leaping may have served all the follow-
ing purposes *except*
   a. entertainment.
   b. religious ritual.
   c. training for warriors.
   d. preparation of bulls for sacrifice.

____4. After Crete's decline, the most powerful
traders along the Mediterranean were the
   a. Aryans.
   b. Minoans.
   c. Africans.
   d. Phoenicians.

____5. The greatest Phoenician colony was in
   a. Carthage.
   b. Crete.
   c. Minoa.
   d. Sardinia.

____6. The Phoenician writing system was based
on
   a. pictographs.
   b. phonetics.
   c. cuneiform.
   d. hieroglyphics.

____7. Popular Phoenician trade items included
   a. obsidian products and religious artifacts.
   b. cotton cloth and wool.
   c. gold, wine, and cotton cloth.
   d. papyrus, purple cloth, and cedar.

____8. One significant Phoenician contribution to
learning was
   a. the writing of many religious texts.
   b. their enhanced system of numbers.
   c. the development of an alphabet.
   d. the training of many learned scholars.

Name _____ Date _____

RETEACHING ACTIVITY *The Origins of Judaism*

Drawing Conclusions

Complete the chart below by indicating the significance of each person, place, or object to the development of Judaism.

PERSON, PLACE, OR EVENT	SIGNIFICANCE
Canaan	1.
Hebrews	2.
Torah	3.
Moses	4.
Ten Commandments	5.

Determining Main Ideas

Write your answers in the blanks provided.

6. Considered the father of the Hebrew people: _____

7. The belief in a single god: _____

8. The god of the Hebrew people: _____

9. A group of people who threatened the Hebrews' position in ancient Palestine: _____

_____

10. Name for the new Hebrew kingdom united under Saul, David, and Solomon: _____

_____

11. Money paid by a weaker power to a stronger power in order to keep the peace: _____

_____

12. First religion to teach monotheism: _____

Name _____ Date _____

CHAPTER 4
Section 1

GUIDED READING *The Egyptian and Nubian Empires*

A. *Following Chronological Order* As you read about the Egyptian Empire, fill in the chart below with the dates and achievements of the rulers listed.

Name of Ruler	Time of Reign	Achievements
Queen Ahhotep		
Hatshepsut		
Thutmose III		
Ramses II		
Libyan pharaohs		
Piankhi		

B. *Clarifying* Explain the relationship between Egypt and **Nubia.**

_____

_____

_____

C. *Comparing and Contrasting* On the back of this paper, compare and contrast the Kushite kingdom in **Meroë** to Egypt's **New Kingdom.**

Name _____ Date _____

GUIDED READING *The Assyrian Empire*

A. *Summarizing* As you read about the rise and fall of the Assyrian Empire, fill in
the diagram below.

Weapons and equipment

Military tactics

Assyrian Empire

Method of governing

Culture

B. *Writing Expository Paragraphs* Explain why the Assyrian Empire collapsed.
Use the names **Nineveh, Medes,** and **Chaldeans** in your explanation.

Name _____ Date _____

A. *Comparing and Contrasting* As you read about the Persian Empire, take notes to fill in the Venn diagram below to compare the reign of King Cyrus with that of King Darius.

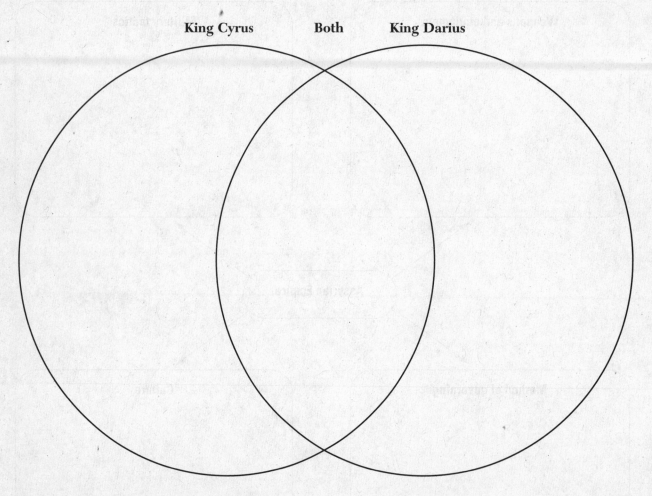

King Cyrus   **Both**   **King Darius**

B. *Writing for a Specific Purpose* Explain how Darius used **satraps** and the **Royal Road** to hold his vast empire together.

_____

_____

_____

C. *Summarizing* On the back of this paper, describe the basic beliefs of the religion founded by **Zoroaster.**

Name _____ Date _____

CHAPTER
4

Section 4

GUIDED READING *The Unification of China*

A. *Summarizing* As you read this section, take notes summarizing the basic ideas of
the following Chinese philosophies.

1. Confucianism	Ideas about social order:	Ideas about government:
Founder:		

2. Daoism	Ideas about order and harmony:	Ideas about a universal force:
Founder:		

3. Legalists	Ideas about social order:	Ideas about government:
Founder:		

B. *Synthesizing* On the back of this paper, explain the concept of
yin and yang. How did this concept contribute to Chinese culture?

C. *Writing for a Specific Purpose* On the back of this paper, explain conditions
in China during the **Qin Dynasty** under the rule of **Shi Huangdi.**

CHAPTER 4 BUILDING VOCABULARY *First Age of Empires*

A. *Matching* Match the description in the second column with the term or name in the first column. Write the appropriate letter next to the word.

____ 1. Hatshepsut

____ 2. Ramses II

____ 3. Kush

____ 4. Assyria

____ 5. Nebuchadnezzar

____ 6. Cyrus

____ 7. Darius

____ 8. Shi Huangdi

a. Nubian kingdom that developed an empire along the Nile River in the 700s B.C.

b. Persian king who founded a huge empire and became known for his tolerance

c. the founder of unified China

d. Mesopotamian society that built a large empire in Southwest Asia through military conquest

e. female New Kingdom pharaoh who encouraged trade instead of just waging war

f. king who extended the Persian empire into India and used a network of roads and standardized coins to promote trade

g. Chaldean king who restored Babylon and built its famous hanging gardens

h. one of the greatest builders of the New Kingdom pharaohs

B. *Completion* Select the term or name that best completes the sentence.

autocracy	New Kingdom	Medes	Zoroaster
Meroë	Royal Road	Nineveh	bureaucracy

1. During the _____, Egypt built an empire and became wealthier and more powerful than ever before.

2. The _____ was a famous road in the Persian Empire that ran 1,677 miles from Susa in Persia to Sardis in Anatolia.

3. The Persian prophet who founded a religion based on the idea that life is a struggle between good and evil was _____.

4. The Assyrian capital that held one of the ancient world's largest libraries was _____.

5. A _____ is a trained civil service.

6. A government that has unlimited power and uses it in an arbitrary manner is an _____.

C. *Writing* Write a paragraph summarizing the philosophies that were promoted in China during the decline of the Zhou Dynasty using the following terms.

Confucius   Daoism   Legalism   *I Ching*   yin and yang

CHAPTER
4

Section 4

SKILLBUILDER PRACTICE *Analyzing Causes and Recognizing Effects*

In 221 B.C., the Qin Dynasty replaced the Zhou Dynasty that had ruled China for about 800 years. To learn more about the causes and effects of the decline of the Zhou Dynasty, read the passage below. As you read, notice that causes and effects can be both short-term and long-term and that effects can turn into causes. Then complete the cause-and-effect diagram below. (See Skillbuilder Handbook)

Nobles Gain Power The Zhou Dynasty set up a feudal state. Local areas were ruled by nobles who pledged their loyalty to the king and raised armies to keep order and protect the kingdom. For the first 300 years, the Zhou Empire remained peaceful and stable.

Beginning in 771 B.C., China expanded into the Chang Jiang basin. As a result of expansion, strong nobles began to use their armies to take over the lands of weaker nobles and consolidate their power. As their power grew, the warlords claimed to be kings in their own territory. Without the loyalty and protection of their feudal nobles, the Zhou Dynasty weakened.

The Qin Dynasty Emerges Beginning around 456 B.C., feudal states were at constant war with one another. The number of feudal states decreased, but those that survived became more powerful. During this "warring states" period, traditional Chinese values collapsed. Chaos, disobedience, and bloody warfare replaced love of order, harmony, and respect for authority. Powerless to end the fighting and restore order, the Zhou Dynasty finally collapsed in 256 B.C. A power struggle followed between the kings of the remaining feudal states. In 221 B.C., the ruler of Qin conquered his rivals, seized control of China, and started a new dynasty.

1. Cause: Period of peace ends; China expands into Chang Jiang basin.

▼

2. Effect/Cause:

▼

3. Effect/Cause: Powerful warlords gain power and set themselves up as kings of their territories.

▼

4. Effect:

▼

5. Cause: Feudal states continue to war against each other.

▼

6. Effect/Cause:

▼

7. Effect/Cause: Unable to restore order, the Zhou Dynasty collapses.

▼

8. Effect:

CHAPTER
4
Section 2

GEOGRAPHY APPLICATION: PLACE *Babylon*

Directions: Read the paragraphs below and study the map carefully. Then answer the questions that follow.

Chaldean King Nebuchadnezzar rebuilt the city of Babylon around 600 B.C., after defeating the mighty Assyrians. He restored the city as the center of his new empire 1,000 years after the death of Hammurabi, the former king of ancient Babylon. All of Babylon, however, was not luxury and splendor. The houses of Babylon were huddled closely together on top of uneven ground. Houses were often built and rebuilt on top of each other without a fresh foundation. In addition, Babylon did not have an adequate garbage removal system. People simply tossed their trash onto the street, creating many social and physical problems.

Nevertheless, Babylon provided a variety of unique sites, such as the stone and wooden bridge that crossed the ancient Euphrates River. Most other cities simply used a collection of boats. Nebuchadnezzar also constructed a new temple and palace buildings, complete with the paved Processional Way.

Nebuchadnezzar took special care when building the defenses for his city. He built a double row of walls reputed to be 150 feet thick, with towers 90 feet high stretching along the perimeter.

At the time, Babylon was the largest city in the world. It covered an area of almost 2,500 acres—an area equal to nearly 2,470 football fields.

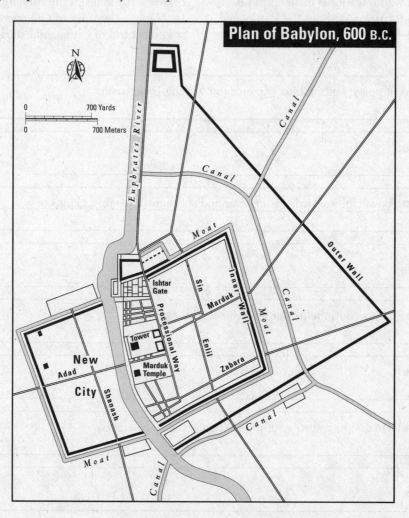

Plan of Babylon, 600 B.C.

Interpreting Text and Visuals

1. How many yards long is the city? _____

2. What is the name of the street that cuts through the center of the city and outside the city follows the Euphrates River? _____

   _____

3. What area of Babylon does not enjoy the protection of the double wall defenses? _____

   _____

   _____

4. What advantages and disadvantages would a bridge give the people of Babylon as opposed to a collection of boats? _____

   _____

   _____

   _____

5. Identify the three bodies of water found in Babylon.

   _____

   Explain what uses these three types of water might have had, including benefits and any potential problems with them. _____

   _____

   _____

   _____

6. Identify the several defenses the illustration shows for Babylon. _____

   _____

   Describe the use for each of the defenses of the city. _____

   _____

   _____

   _____

CHAPTER 4

Section 2

PRIMARY SOURCE *from* Assyrian Capture
of Jerusalem

by Sennacherib

In 701 B.C. an Assyrian king, Sennacherib, launched a bloody campaign against several princes of Phoenicia and Palestine and captured the city of Jerusalem. What does this passage from an official record of Sennacherib's conquests tell you about Assyria's military power?

In the continuation of my campaign I besieged Beth-Dagon, Joppa, Banai-Barqa, Azuru, cities belonging to Sidqia who did not bow to my feet quickly enough; I conquered them and carried their spoils away. The officials, the patricians and the common people of Ekron—who had thrown Padi, their king, into fetters because he was loyal to his solemn oath sworn by the god Ashur, and had handed him over to [king] Hezekiah, the Jew—and he (Hezekiah) held him in prison, unlawfully, as if he (Padi) be an enemy—had become afraid and had called for help upon the kings of Egypt and the bowmen, the chariot-corps and the cavalry of the king of Ethiopia, an army beyond counting—and they had come to their assistance. In the plain of Eltekeh, their battle lines were drawn up against me and they sharpened their weapons. Upon a trust-inspiring oracle given by Ashur, my lord, I fought with them and inflicted a defeat upon them. In the mêlée of the battle, I personally captured alive the Egyptian charioteers with their princes and also the charioteers of the king of Ethiopia. I besieged Eltekeh and Timnah, conquered them and carried their spoils away. I assaulted Ekron and killed the officials and patricians who had committed the crime and hung their bodies on poles surrounding the city. The common citizens who were guilty of minor crimes, I considered prisoners of war. The rest of them, those who were not accused of crimes and misbehavior, I released. I made Padi, their king, come from Jerusalem and set him as their lord on the throne, imposing upon him the tribute due to me as overlord.

As to Hezekiah, the Jew, he did not submit to my yoke, I laid siege to 46 of his strong cities, walled forts and to the countless small villages in their vicinity, and conquered them by means of well-stamped earth-ramps, and battering-rams brought thus near to the walls combined with the attack by foot soldiers, using mines, breeches as well as sapper work. I drove out of them 200,150 people,

young and old, male and female, horses, mules, donkeys, camels, big and small cattle beyond counting, and considered them booty. Himself I made a prisoner in Jerusalem, his royal residence, like a bird in a cage. I surrounded him with earth-work in order to molest those who were leaving his city's gate. His towns which I had plundered, I took away from his country and gave them over to Mitinti, king of Ashdod, Padi, king of Ekron, and Sillibel, king of Gaza. Thus I reduced his country, but I still increased the tribute and the *katrû*-presents due to me as his overlord which I imposed later upon him beyond the former tribute, to be delivered annually. Hezekiah himself, whom the terror-inspiring spendor of my lordship had overwhelmed and whose irregular and elite troops which he had brought into Jerusalem, his royal residence, in order to strengthen it, had deserted him, did send me, later, to Nineveh, my lordly city, together with 30 talents of gold, 800 talents of silver, precious stones, antimony, large cuts of red stone, couches inlaid with ivory, *nîmedu*-chairs inlaid with ivory, elephant-hides, ebony-wood, box-wood, and all kinds of valuable treasures, his own daughters, concubines, male and female musicians. In order to deliver the tribute and to do obeisance as a slave he sent his personal messenger.

from James B. Pritchard, ed., *Ancient Near Eastern Texts*, 2nd ed. (Princeton, New Jersey: Princeton University Press, 1955), 287ff. Reprinted in *The Ancient World to A.D. 300*, 2nd ed. (New York: The Macmillan Company, 1968), 6–7.

Activity Options

1. ***Writing for a Specific Purpose*** Write a headline about Sennacherib's military exploits from the point of view of either an Assyrian or a resident of one of the conquered cities.

2. ***Developing Historical Perspective*** With a partner, conduct an in-depth interview with Sennacherib about his military campaign.

CHAPTER
4
Section 3

PRIMARY SOURCE "To the Fire"
from the Zend-Avesta

The Avesta is the sacred book of the Persian religion founded by Zoroaster. It contains prayers, invocations, religious teachings, and hymns that praise Zoroastrian gods. The Zend-Avesta includes the original book and commentaries added through the years. "To the Fire" is chanted during a fire-worship ritual in which a priest dressed in a white robe and veil invokes the power of the supreme god Ahura Mazda; consecrates sacred water, a bundle of twigs, and the juice of a sacred plant; and then kindles the fire. As you read this hymn, think about what believers in Zoroastrianism ask Fire to grant them.

I offer my sacrifice and homage to thee, the Fire, as a good offering, and an offering with our hail of salvation, even as an offering of praise with benedictions, to thee, the Fire, O Ahura Mazda's son! Meet for sacrifice art thou, and worthy of our homage. And as meet for sacrifice, and thus worthy of our homage, mayest thou be in the houses of men who worship Mazda. Salvation be to this man who worships thee in verity and truth, with wood in hand, and Baresma ready, with flesh in hand, and holding too the mortar. And mayest thou be ever fed with wood as the prescription orders. Yea, mayest thou have thy perfume justly, and thy sacred butter without fail, and thine andirons regularly placed. Be of full-age as to thy nourishment, . . . O Fire, Ahura Mazda's son! Be now aflame within this house; be ever without fail in flame; be all a-shine within this house; . . . for long time be thou thus to the furtherance of the heroic renovation, to the completion of all progress, yea, even till the good heroic millennial time when that renovation shall have become complete. Give me, O Fire, Ahura Mazda's son! a speedy glory, speedy nourishment, and speedy booty, and . . . an expanded mind, and nimbleness of tongue for soul and understanding, even an understanding continually growing in its largeness, and that never wanders, and long enduring virile power, an offspring sure of foot, that never sleeps on watch, and that rises quick from bed, and likewise a wakeful offspring, helpful to nurture, . . . keeping order in men's meetings, yea, drawing men to assemblies through their influence and word, grown to power, skillful, redeeming others from oppression, served by many followers, which may advance my line in prosperity, and fame, and my Vis, and my Bantu, and my province, yea, an offering which may deliver orders to the Province as firm and righteous rulers. And mayest thou grant

me, O Fire, Ahura Mazda's Son! that whereby instructors may be given me, now and for evermore, giving light to me of Heaven, the best life of the saints, brilliant, all glorious. And may I have experience of the good reward, and the good renown, and of the long forecasting preparation of the soul. The Fire of Ahura Mazda addresses this admonition to all for whom he cooks the night and morning meal. From all these, O Spitama! he wishes to secure good care, . . . the care of a true praiser. At both the hands of all who come by me, I, the Fire, keenly look: What brings the mate to his mate, the one who walks at large, to him who sits at home? We worship the bounteous Fire, the swift-driving charioteer. And if this man who passes brings him wood brought with sacred care, or if he brings the Baresma spread with sanctity, or the Hadhâ-naêpata plant, then afterwards Ahura Mazda's Fire will bless him, contented, not offended, and in its satisfaction saying thus: May a herd of kine be with thee, and a multitude of men, may an active mind go with thee, and an active soul as well. As a blest soul mayest thou live through thy life, the nights which thou shall live. This is the blessing of the Fire for him who brings it wood well dried, sought out for flaming, purified with the earnest blessing of the sacred ritual truth.

from James Darmestetter, trans., the Zend-Avesta. Reprinted in Epiphanius Wilson, ed., Sacred Books of the East (New York: P. F. Collier & Son, 1900), 106–107.

Discussion Questions

Clarifying

1. According to "To the Fire," what will the man who worships Fire receive in return?
2. What helps nourish Fire?
3. ***Making Inferences*** Do you think Fire signifies truth and light or evil and darkness? Explain.

PRIMARY SOURCE *from* **Intrigues of the Warring States**

This selection is from an anonymous work called Chan Kuo Ts'e *(Intrigues of the Warring States). Probably written in the early part of the second century* B.C., *the Chan Kuo Ts'e relates the history and fables of the latter Zhou Dynasty and offers a wealth of advice on the way states should be governed. The problems described in this excerpt led to the decline of the Zhou Dynasty and to the rise of new political ideas and philosophies. How does Ying-hou think that King Chao should govern Ch'in?*

"Your majesty has doubtless heard about the Spirit of the Grove in the country of Hanker?" Ying-hou asked King Chao of Ch'in. "There lived in Hanker an extremely rash youth who got the Sacred Grove to gamble with him. 'If I beat you,' said the boy, 'you must lend me your genie for three days. If I lose to you, you may do as you please with me.' So saying, he cast the dice for the Grove with his left hand and for himself with his right. The Grove lost and lent the boy his genie for three days. But when the Grove went back to get his Spirit, he was turned away. Five days later the Grove began to rot and in seven it had died.

"The country of Ch'in is your majesty's Grove and power is its genie: is it not a course fraught with danger to lend it to others? Now I have never heard of a finger being greater than an arm nor of an arm being greater than a leg, but if such should exist it could only indicate a serious disease!

"A hundred men scrambling to fetch a gourd by cart will accomplish less than one man holding it in his hand and walking purposefully. For if the hundred actually managed to get it aboard their wagon you may be quite sure that the gourd would be split asunder when it arrived. Today the country of Ch'in is used by Lord Hua-yang, by Jang-hou, by the Queen Mother and by your majesty. If it is not to become a gourd with which any may dip his water this should stop. For you may be quite sure that when a country does become a gourd for all to dip with, it too will be split asunder.

"I have heard it said, 'when the fruit is heavy the bough is strained, when the bough is strained the trunk is harmed; when a capital is great it endangers the state, when a minister is strong he menaces his king.' Yet in your city today every man worth more than a peck of grain is the minister's man—this includes your majesty's lieutenants, chancellors, and even personal attendants. Even in times of peace this should not happen, but should there ever be trouble, then I would certainly wit-

ness a king standing all alone in his own court.

"I have the temerity to feel fear for your majesty. And what I fear is that in the country of Ch'in, many generations hence, the rulers will no longer be descendants of yours.

"Your servant has heard that the awesome presence of great rulers in the past held their ministers in check at home and spread their control abroad over the land. Their government was neither troubled nor seditious and their deputies trod a straight path, fearing to do otherwise. But today the deputies of Jang-hou split the lords among themselves, and tallies given by his hand are recognized all over the land. He arrogates the power of a great state to muster troops and attack the lords, but the profits from his victories and gains all return to his own fief of T'ao, the spoils enter the treasuries of the Queen Mother and revenues from within your borders find their way to Lord Hua-yang. Surely what used to be called 'the road to danger and destruction for state and ruler' begins here.

"If three honored persons can drain the state to secure themselves, can the king's power be absolute? Will all commands originate with him? In truth, your majesty, only one in every three actually does."

from J.I. Crump, trans., *Chan-Kuo Ts'e,* "Intrigues of the Warring States." Reprinted in Cyril Birch, ed., *Anthology of Chinese Literature: From Early Times to the Fourteenth Century* (New York: Grove Press, 1965), 39–40.

Discussion Questions

1. **Determining Main Ideas** According to Ying-hou, what is wrong with the way that King Chao rules Ch'in?
2. **Summarizing** What examples does Ying-hou use to strengthen his argument against the way King Chao rules?
3. **Drawing Conclusions** What advice do you think Ying-hou might give to the king about governing Ch'in more effectively?

CHAPTER 4

Section 4

PRIMARY SOURCE *from the* Analects
by Confucius

The Analects, *a collection of the teachings of Confucius, was compiled by his students in about 400 B.C. In this excerpt the "Master"—Confucius—expresses his views on being a gentleman. What values and attitudes does Confucius promote?*

The Master said, If a gentleman is frivolous, he will lose the respect of his inferiors and lack firm ground upon which to build up his education. First and foremost he must learn to be faithful to his superiors, to keep promises, to refuse the friendship of all who are not like him. And if he finds he has made a mistake, then he must not be afraid of admitting the fact and amending his ways.

Tzu-kung asked about the true gentleman. The Master said, He does not preach what he practises till he has practised what he preaches.

The Master said, A gentleman can see a question from all sides without bias. The small man is biased and can see a question only from one side.

The Master said, A gentleman in his dealings with the world has neither enmities nor affections; but wherever he sees Right he ranges himself beside it.

The Master said, A gentleman takes as much trouble to discover what is right as lesser men take to discover what will pay.

The Master said, A gentleman covets the reputation of being slow in word but prompt in deed.

The Master said, A gentleman who is widely versed in letters and at the same time knows how to submit his learning to the restraints of ritual is not likely, I think, to go far wrong.

The Master said, A true gentleman is calm and at ease; the Small Man is fretful and ill at ease.

At home in his native village his manner is simple and unassuming, as though he did not trust himself to speak. But in the ancestral temple and at Court he speaks readily, though always choosing his words with care.

At Court when conversing with the Under Ministers his attitude is friendly and affable; when conversing with the Upper Ministers, it is restrained and formal. When the ruler is present it is wary, but not cramped.

When the ruler summons him to receive a guest, a look of confusion comes over his face and his legs seem to give beneath his weight.

When the guest has gone, he reports the close of the visit, saying, "The guest is no longer looking back."

On entering the Palace Gate he seems to shrink into himself, as though there were not room. If he halts, it must never be in the middle of the gate, nor in going through does he ever tread on the threshold. As he passes the Stance a look of confusion comes over his face, his legs seem to give way under him and words seem to fail him. While, holding up the hem of his skirt, he ascends the Audience Hall, he seems to double up and keeps in his breath, so that you would think he was not breathing at all. On coming out, after descending the first step his expression relaxes into one of satisfaction and relief. At the bottom of the steps he quickens his pace, advancing with an air of majestic dignity. On regaining his place he resumes his attitude of wariness and hesitation.

from Confucius, *The Analects of Confucius,* Arthur Waley, trans. (London: George Allen and Unwin, Ltd., 1938). Reprinted in Peter N. Stearns, ed., *Documents in World History,* Vol. 1 (New York: HarperCollins, 1988), 36–37.

Activity Options

1. *Summarizing Written Texts* Write a list of *do's* and *don'ts* based on these teachings of Confucius. Share your list with the class.
2. *Synthesizing* With a partner, role-play a discussion about the nature of a true gentleman between Confucius and his student Tzu-kung.

Name _____ Date _____

CHAPTER 4

Section 1

LITERATURE SELECTION "Ozymandias"
by Percy Bysshe Shelley

This poem by English poet Percy Bysshe Shelley (1792–1822) refers to Egyptian pharaoh Ramses II, whose Greek name is Ozymandias. During his reign, Ramses II had several temples built that were adorned with massive statues of himself. The temple where he was buried, the Ramesseum, featured an inscription similar to the one in the poem and a 1,000-ton statue of Ramses II. What is Shelley's opinion of Ramses II and his monuments?

I met a traveler from an antique land
Who said: Two vast and trunkless legs of stone
Stand in the desert. Near them, on the sand,
Half sunk, a shattered visage lies, whose frown,
And wrinkled lip, and sneer of cold command,
Tell that its sculptor well those passions read
Which yet survive, stamped on these lifeless things,
The hand that mocked them and the heart that fed;
And on the pedestal these words appear:
"My name is Ozymandias, king of kings:
Look on my works, ye Mighty, and despair!"
Nothing beside remains. Round the decay
Of that colossal wreck, boundless and bare
The lone and level sands stretch far away.

Percy Bysshe Shelley, "Ozymandias." Reprinted in
An Introduction to Poetry (Boston: Little, Brown,
1966), 253–254.

Research Options

1. *Using Visual Stimuli* Find photographs of archaeological artifacts associated with Ramses II. Then choose and copy a photograph that you think best illustrates this poem.

2. *Drawing Conclusionsp* Use the Internet, a print or on-line encyclopedia, or a book about ancient Egypt to find out more about Ramses II. Then discuss with classmates whether you agree with Shelley's view of the pharaoh in this poem.

CHAPTER 4

Section 2

LITERATURE SELECTION "The Destruction of Sennacherib"
by George Gordon, Lord Byron

In this poem, English poet George Gordon, Lord Byron (1788–1824) retells the Biblical story in II Kings 19:35. In this story, Assyria's King Sennacherib suddenly loses his army while leading an attack on Jerusalem. What images or sensory details in the poem help you picture what happens?

The Assyrian came down like the wolf on the fold,
And his cohorts were gleaming in purple and gold;
And the sheen of their spears was like stars on the sea,
When the blue wave rolls nightly on deep Galilee.

Like the leaves of the forest when summer is green,
That host with their banners at sunset were seen:
Like the leaves of the forest when autumn hath blown,
That host on the morrow lay withered and strown.

For the Angel of death spread his wings on the blast,
And breathed in the face of the foe as he passed;
And the eyes of the sleepers waxed deadly and chill,
And their hearts but once heaved—and for ever grew still!

And there lay the steed with his nostril all wide,
But through it there rolled not the breath of his pride;
And the foam of his gasping lay white on the turf,
And cold as the spray of the rock-beating surf.

And there lay the rider distorted and pale,
With the dew on his brow, and the rust on his mail;
And the tents were all silent, the banners alone,
The lances unlifted, the trumpet unblown.

And the widows of Ashur are loud in their wail,
And the idols are broke in the temple of Baal;
And the might of the Gentile, unsmote by the sword,
Hath melted like snow in the glance of the Lord!

George Gordon, Lord Byron, "The
Destruction of Sennacherib." Reprinted in
X. J. Kennedy, *An Introduction to Poetry*
(Boston: Little, Brown, 1966), 152–153.

Research Options

1. ***Comparing and Contrasting*** Look up and
read the Bible story of Sennacherib in II Kings
19:35. Then discuss with a small group of classmates similarities and differences between the
two versions of the story.

2. ***Clarifying*** Research the following allusions in
the poem: Galilee in line 4, Ashur in line 21, and
Baal in line 22. Then share your findings with
classmates.

CHAPTER 4

Section 3

LITERATURE SELECTION "Babylon"
by Alfred, Lord Tennyson

Alfred, Lord Tennyson was a popular 19th-century English poet. "Babylon" refers to the conquest of the Babylonians by Cyrus, king of Persia. Does Tennyson feel that the Babylonians deserve their fate?

"Come down, and sit in the dust, O virgin
  daughter of Babylon; sit on the ground:
there is no throne."—Isaiah 47: 1

Bow, daughter of Babylon, bow thee to dust!
Thine heart shall be quell'd, and thy pride shall
  be crush'd:
Weep, Babylon, weep! for thy splendour is past;
And they come like the storm in the day of the
  blast.

How, desolate Babylon, lost one and lone!
And bind thee in sack-cloth—for where is thy
  throne?
Like a wine-press in wrath will I trample thee
  down.
And rend from thy temples the pride of thy crown.

Though thy streets be a hundred, thy gates be all
  brass.
Yet thy proud ones of war shall be wither'd like
  grass;
Thy gates shall be broken, thy strength be laid low.
And thy streets shall resound to the shouts of the
  foe!

Though thy chariots of power on thy battlements
  bound.
And the grandeur of waters encompass thee
  round;
Yet thy walls shall be shaken, thy waters shall fail.
Thy matrons shall shriek, and thy king shall be
  pale.

The terrible day of thy fall is at hand,
When my rage shall descend on the face of thy
  land;
The lances are pointed, the keen sword is bar'd,
The shields are anointed, the helmets prepar'd.

I call upon Cyrus! He comes from afar.
And the armies of nations are gather'd to war;
With the blood of thy children his path shall be
  red,
And the bright sun of conquest shall blaze o'er
  his head!

Thou glory of kingdoms! thy princes are drunk,
But their loins shall be loos'd, and their hearts
  shall be sunk;
They shall crouch to the dust, and be counted as
  slaves,
At the roll of his wheels, like the rushing of waves!

For I am the Lord, who have mightily spann'd
The breadth of the heavens, and the sea and the
  land:
And the mountains shall flow at my presence,
  and earth
Shall reel to and fro in the glance of my wrath!

Your proud domes of cedar on earth shall be
  thrown.
And the rank grass shall wave o'er the lonely
  hearthstone:
And your sons and your sires and your daughters
  shall bleed
By the barbarous hands of the murdering Mede!

I will sweep ye away in destruction and death.
As the whirlwind that scatters the chaff with its
  breath:
And the fanes of your gods shall be sprinkled
  with gore,
And the course of your stream shall be heard of
  no more.

There the wandering Arab shall ne'er pitch his tent.
But the beasts of the desert shall wail and lament:
In their desolate houses the dragons shall lie,
And the satyrs shall dance, and the bittern shall
  cry!

Alfred, Lord Tennyson, "Babylon." Reprinted in W. J. Rolfe,
ed., *The Complete Poetical Works of Tennyson* (Boston:
Houghton Mifflin, 1898), 775.

Activity Options

1. ***Comparing and Contrasting*** Compare the
   views expressed on the empires in
   "Ozymandias," "The Destruction of
   Sennacherib," and "Babylon."
2. ***Writing from Models*** Write your own poem
   about one of the empires you have read about.

Name _____ Date _____

HISTORYMAKERS Hatshepsut

Ambitious Queen Seeking Eternity

"My command stands firm like the mountains, and the sun's disk shines and spreads rays over . . . my august person, and my falcon rises high above the kingly banner unto all eternity."—inscription ordered by Hatshepsut

Hatshepsut was a remarkable woman. Born to the Egyptian royal family, she was not content to play the secondary role of queen. When given the opportunity, she seized control and ruled Egypt for two decades.

There are three other players in the story of the queen, and they all have the same name. Thutmose I, pharaoh from around 1525 B.C., was her father. He was also father to Thutmose II. Hatshepsut and Thutmose II, who had different mothers, were married to one another. This was the custom in Egypt's royal family. Thutmose II, then, was both Hatshepsut's half-brother and her husband. Thutmose II's son, Thutmose III, was born to another woman. He was Hatshepsut's nephew and stepson.

When Thutmose I died, the crown passed to his oldest surviving son, Thutmose II. Hatshepsut, as his wife, ruled as queen. They ruled together for eight years. During that time Thutmose III was born.

Suddenly, Thutmose II—though only in his early thirties—died. Thutmose III, his successor, was only a few years old. Hatshepsut ruled with him as co-regent. In the earliest artwork from his reign, Thutmose III is shown as the chief ruler. Hatshepsut is placed behind him, which indicates junior status.

This arrangement did not last. In the second year of their joint rule, Hatshepsut made her move and seized power. In 1503 B.C., she had herself declared king. She began to wear the double crown that showed she ruled upper and lower Egypt. In later years she was even shown in artwork wearing male clothing. To support her claim to the throne, Hatshepsut resorted to propaganda. She had a temple built and decorated with images showing that she was born of the gods—as a proper pharaoh should be. She also spread a false story that Thutmose I had arranged to have her crowned king.

The real support for her power grab, though, was a strong group of court officials, including the chief steward, the high priest, the chancellor, and the treasurer. She did not have Thutmose III killed, but for almost 20 years she ran the country.

During this time, there was little military activity. The woman king did work to expand Egyptian trade, however. She sent workers to Sinai to mine turquoise. She also launched a large expedition to Punt, an African land that was located on the southern edge of the Red Sea and the home of such desirable goods as myrrh and frankincense. Egyptian priests wanted these substances—both of which were incense—to burn during sacred ceremonies. Hatshepsut also sent agents with weapons and jewelry to trade. They brought back not only the incense, but also several trees and roots to plant in Egypt to produce this valuable substance.

Pictures showing this voyage appear on the walls of a great temple that Hatshepsut had built. Another set of scenes depicts a different venture. Early in her rule, Hatshepsut ordered red granite taken from a quarry on the Nile River. The stone was shaped into two huge obelisks 185 feet high. They were placed on a barge 300 feet long and 100 feet wide. Twenty-seven ships powered by 864 men pulling oars towed the stones down river to the temple at Karnak. Before being set in place, they were completely covered with gold—and inscribed with Hatshepsut's name.

After more than 20 years, though, Thutmose III was ready to rule on his own. In 1482 B.C., he took control from his aunt. No one knows what happened to Hatshepsut. Soon after beginning his rule, though, Thutmose III tried to remove her memory from Egypt. Almost all mention of her, on stone or on papyrus, was erased. Nevertheless, one of her two great obelisks now stands in Cairo. It calls her by the title she so dearly wanted—pharaoh.

Questions

1. *Making Inferences* Why would the support of court officials help Hatshepsut seize power?
2. *Summarizing* For what achievements is Hatshepsut remembered?
3. *Drawing Conclusions* Why would Thutmose III try to remove Hatshepsut's name from all records?

HISTORYMAKERS # Sennacherib
Destroyer and Builder of Cities

"The flame that consumes those who will not submit."
and "He who cares for Assyria."—Assyrian inscriptions describing Sennacherib

Sennacherib's Assyrian army often sent waves of fear through cities and peoples who found themselves in its path. Sennacherib was widely known for brutal treatment of those who would not submit to his will. On the other hand, to Assyrians themselves, Sennacherib was a great leader who expanded Assyrian power and rebuilt the great city of Nineveh.

Sennacherib was the son of Sargon II, who had helped build the Assyrian Empire in Southwest Asia. Under Sargon the Assyrians had captured the ancient city of Babylon. In addition, he had formed an efficient and effective government. Sennacherib, the crown prince, had been part of that government. When his father died in 705 B.C., he took the throne. The new king devoted the first years of his reign to a great building project.

Nineveh, an ancient city, had fallen into disrepair. Sennacherib was determined to make it his capital—and a more glorious city than it had ever been. He made the city's walls stronger and built new streets. He built a huge palace on eight acres of ground. It included parks and orchards with plants and animals from around the world. The palace was decorated with silver and copper. Copper was also used to make huge statues of 12 bulls and 12 lions. Most important, Sennacherib brought precious water to the city. He built canals to carry water from hills more than 50 miles away. Outside the city walls, he set aside farmland for the city residents. There he introduced an unusual new crop: cotton.

While the king created the capital that was his work of art, trouble brewed in the east. The former king of Babylon—allowed by Sargon to live—decided to reclaim his throne. He attacked in 703 but was quickly defeated by Sennacherib. In response to the threat, the Assyrian king decided to bring the whole area under control. He captured 88 walled towns and several major cities.

Sennacherib also moved to the west. Hezekiah, the king of Judah, had joined in the Babylonian revolt. So, too, had the Phoenician cities of Tyre and Sidon. Representatives of the pharaoh of Egypt had also discussed taking part. Sennacherib decided to attack. In 701 B.C., he captured the Phoenician cities. Then he moved to Judah, where he forced Hezekiah to pay a large penalty. Next came Egypt. As Sennacherib prepared for an invasion, though, he was forced to call a halt. Some disaster—perhaps a plague—struck his army and he had to withdraw.

More military movements were needed in the east. Again, the former king of Babylon began a revolt. Sennacherib used a remarkable feat of engineering to move his troops into position. He sailed ships down the Tigris River to a southern city. Then he had them hauled overland to the Euphrates River. From there they sailed into the Persian Gulf. Sennacherib then easily defeated the allies of the old king of Babylon.

Trouble continued there for many years, however. Sennacherib had tried to maintain Babylon as a separate kingdom, but these attempts failed. The Chaldeans, who lived in Babylon, grew more and more unwilling to recognize Assyrian power. Finally, they captured and killed the king's son and murdered other supporters of Assyria. Sennacherib led an army back to Babylon in 689 B.C. He quickly destroyed the city, killed his opponents, and flooded the ancient capital.

With his conquests complete, Sennacherib settled down in his capital to rule his empire. He named one of his younger sons, Esarhaddon, as his heir—an act that raised resentment among his other sons. Their resentment combined with a Babylonian conspiracy brought about Sennacherib's death. In January of 681 B.C., two sons murdered the aged Sennacherib, perhaps while he was at prayer in a temple.

Questions

1. *Forming and Supporting Opinions* Which inscription at the top of the page do you think is a better description of Sennacherib? Give reasons for your answer.
2. *Drawing Conclusions* Do you think that Sennacherib was resourceful? Why or why not?
3. *Making Inferences* What led Sennacherib to attack other kingdoms?

CONNECTIONS ACROSS TIME AND CULTURES

Empires of Southwest Asia

CHAPTER 4

Section 2

Ancient peoples built great empires along the Mediterranean and in Asia, Arabia, and Africa. As you read in this chapter, through constant and skilled warfare, the Assyrians built a powerful empire in Southwest Asia. Almost a thousand years earlier, the Hittites had been the dominant power in this region. Compare the Hittite and Assyrian empires by filling in the boxes in the chart.

	Hittite Empire	Assyrian Empire
1. Military advantages	Iron weapons, superior chariots	
2. Location of empire	Anatolia, Mesopotamia, and northern Syria	
3. Cultural values	Adapted ideas of advanced cultures they conquered	
4. Time span of empire	About 450 years	
5. Cause of fall	Invaders from the north	
6. Greatest legacy	Spread of knowledge from iron technology	

Name _____ Date _____

Determining Main Ideas

Choose the word that most accurately completes each sentence below. Write that word in the blank provided.

Kush	Hatshepsut	Meroë
Aksum	cuneiform	Piankhi
New Kingdom	Phoenicia	Ramses II
Nubia	Assyrians	Valley of the Kings
dynasty	Hyksos	Thutmose III
Hammurabi		

1. The Asiatic invaders who ruled Egypt from about 1640 to 1570 B.C. were called _____.

2. The time period between about 1570 and 1075 B.C. in Egypt, its third period of glory, was known as the _____.

3. _____ was a female pharaoh who brought great prosperity to Egypt.

4. _____ was a warlike ruler who led a number of victorious invasions into Palestine and Syria and turned Egypt into a mighty empire.

5. Egypt also pushed farther into _____, a region of Africa that straddled the upper Nile River.

6. The Egyptians and Hittites made a peace treaty under the reign of Egyptian pharaoh _____.

7. The area near Thebes where Egyptian rulers of the New Kingdom built splendid tombs was called _____.

8. The Nubian kingdom that interacted heavily with Egypt was _____.

9. King _____ united the Nile Valley and became part of Egypt's Twenty-fifth Dynasty.

10. The Kushites in Egypt were defeated by a war-like people from Southwest Asia called the _____.

11. After being forced out of Egypt, the Kushite royal family moved south to _____.

12. Meroë eventually was defeated by another kingdom located 400 miles to the southeast, _____.

Name _____ Date _____

Reading Comprehension

Find the name or term in the second column that best matches the description in the first column. (Note: Sometimes more than one letter may be required.) Then write the letter of your answer(s) in the blank.

_____ 1. Two means by which Assyria acquired a large empire (two answers)

_____ 2. Assyrian king who burned Babylon and ordered its residents killed

_____ 3. Assyrian system of government management

_____ 4. Capital city of Assyrian culture, the largest city of its day

_____ 5. Assyrian king who established one of the ancient world's largest libraries

_____ 6. Assyrian practice that eventually contributed to the downfall of their empire

_____ 7. A combined army of these two groups destroyed Assyria's capital city (two answers)

_____ 8. Chaldean king who created terraced trees and shrubs for his wife's enjoyment

_____ 9. Capital city of Chaldean empire

_____ 10. One of the seven wonders of the ancient world

_____ 11. Seven-tiered building in Babylon used by Chaldean priests and astronomers

A. Ashurbanipal

B. strong military

C. local governors and a central authority

D. hanging gardens of Babylon

E. cruelty to enemies

F. advanced weapons

G. Medes

H. Sennacherib

I. monarchy

J. Nebuchadnezzar

K. Chaldeans

L. refusal to trade widely

M. Babylon

N. Nineveh

O. ziggurat

Name _____ Date _____

Determining Main Ideas

Complete the chart below by explaining the definition or significance of each of the
following terms and names.

TERM OR NAME		DEFINITION/SIGNIFICANCE
1. Cyrus	→	
2. Cambyses	→	
3. Darius	→	
4. satrap	→	
5. Royal Road	→	
6. Zoroaster	→	

Summarizing

7. What were some characteristics of the Persian Empire under Cyrus?

_____

_____

8. What contributions did Darius make toward the advancement of the Persian Empire?

_____

_____

CHAPTER
4
Section 4

RETEACHING ACTIVITY *The Unification of China*

Determining Main Ideas
Write your answers in the blanks provided.

1. China's most important scholar and teacher whose ideas influenced civilizations throughout East Asia:

   _____

2. Chinese belief in respect for parents and ancestors: _____

3. A trained civil service who runs the government: _____

4. The philosophy of Laozi, who believed that a universal force guides all living things:

   _____

5. Belief that a highly efficient and powerful government was the key to ending civil disorder and restoring
   harmony: _____

6. A book of oracles that provided Chinese people with good advice and simple common sense:

   _____

7. Two powers that together represent the natural rhythms of life and complement each other:

   _____

8. Dynasty that replaced the Zhou Dynasty in China: _____

9. "First Emperor" whose military victories doubled China's size and who strengthened and lengthened
   the Great Wall of China: _____

10. A government with unlimited power that it uses in an arbitrary manner:

    _____

11. Two improvements that took place under Shi Huangdi: _____

    _____

12. Dynasty that took over China around 202 B.C.: _____

Answer Key

Chapter 1, Section 1
GUIDED READING

A. Possible responses:

1. Australopithecines: opposable thumb; first to walk upright

2. *Homo habilis*: small brain; first tool-maker, butcher

3. *Homo erectus*: larger brain, more intelligent; first to use fire, spoken language, migrate

4. Neanderthals: heavy slanted brows, well-developed muscles, thick bones; developed religious beliefs, built temporary shelters

5. Cro-Magnons: identical to modern humans; planned difficult projects, communicated with language

B. Possible responses: Paleolithic Age: began 2.5 million B.C.; ended 8000 B.C.; made stone chopping tools

Neolithic Age: began 8000 B.C.; ended 3000 B.C.; polished stone tools, made pottery, grew crops, raised animals

C. Possible response: Archaeologists examine artifacts uncovered at digs to learn about the technology and other achievements of prehistoric people. Anthropologists study people's culture; paleontologists study and date fossil remains.

Chapter 1, Section 2
GUIDED READING

A. Possible responses:

1. Used stone, bone, and wood to craft special tools to kill game, catch fish and pry plants loose

2. Necklaces, polished beads, carved sculptures of animals, cave paintings

3. Discovery that scattered seeds grew into crops, rising temperatures, rich supply of grain, food demands of small population boom

4. Developed in different places worldwide and spread from centers of agriculture to neighboring regions

5. Obsidian mirrors, jewelry, knives; colorful wall paintings; religious shrines

6. Natural disasters, disease, looting

B. Possible response: Farmers planted crops on land they cleared and fertilized using the slash-and-burn method. Domestication may have begun with the herding of animals into enclosures to be used as a constant source of food.

Chapter 1, Section 3
GUIDED READING

A. Possible responses:

1. Economic changes: Irrigation systems, food surpluses, prosperous economy, new skills and crafts, expanded trade between villages

2. Social changes: Complex social relationships, development of social classes, more organized religion

3. Economic changes: Expansion of trade over a wider area, specialized workers, varied crafts, advanced technology

4. Social changes: Soaring populations, emergence of government to maintain order, system of writing to keep records, formal religious institutions

B. Possible response: Advanced technology and the opportunity for specialization allowed people in Ur to work as artisans, traders, and officials in complex institutions such as government and religion. Scribes invented a system of writing called cuneiform to keep track of rituals and barter transactions between farmers and merchants. The center of life in Ur was the ziggurat, a massive temple.

Chapter 1
BUILDING VOCABULARY

A. Matching

1. g
2. d
3. b
4. f
5. c
6. a
7. h
8. e

B. Completion

1. nomad
2. barter
3. cuneiform
4. culture
5. Neolithic Revolution
6. slash-and-burn farming

C. Writing

Possible Answer

As early people spread out over the world and adapted to different environments, they developed new <u>technology</u> in order to survive. New tools, weapons, and techniques helped communities thrive. In addition, the <u>domestication</u> of animals and the development of farming brought great changes in human life. A steady source of food allowed people to settle in one place. Villages eventually grew into cities, where the need for <u>specialization</u> arose. Food surpluses allowed individuals to become experts at a variety of crafts. The large populations of cities also created the need for government and other <u>institutions</u>. Within the complex cultures of cities, the first civilizations arose.

Chapter 1, Section 1
SKILLBUILDER PRACTICE

1. north, east, and south

2. North America, South America, Australia

3. nearly 9,000 kilometers (more than 6,000 miles)

Possible responses:

4. Students may mention climate, glaciers, landforms, and the availability of food and water.

5. a. Africa, Europe, and Asia

   b. all continents shown

   c. Migrations of early humans spanned an enormous period of time beginning 1.6 million years ago.

6. Early humans were able to adapt and survive in many different environments. They were intelligent enough to develop tools and skills needed to migrate over great distances and varied terrain. They occupied virtually every part of the earth, except ice-covered regions, by 12,000 years ago.

Chapter 1, Section 2
GEOGRAPHY APPLICATION

Responses may vary on the inferential questions. Sample responses are given for those.

1. They used ladders to get in and out, and moved from house to house on the roofs.

2. It was located in a hilly section of what is now Turkey.

3. Catal Huyuk was built near a small stream and three volcanoes.

4. The village was made of mud-dried bricks and the dwellings were connected on one or more sides to other dwellings. Roofs were made of woven mud and reeds. Each unit had a hearth and sleeping area. People entered their dwellings through holes in the roof.

5. The people are believed to have been very religious. They built elaborate religious shrines to a goddess. In various paintings she is shown giving birth, nursing a child, or living as an old woman with a vulture.

6. Answers will vary. Students may suggest that people would have been able to travel more easily. As a result, they may have left the village and it may not have lasted as long. Trade would have been greater, however, and more people may have discovered Catal Huyuk. A river would have affected their agricultural system and the crops they grew.

7. The close-knit construction of living units minimized exterior walls and may have been a protection against wild animals or human enemies. The close living quarters probably reinforced the sense of community.

Chapter 1, Section 1
PRIMARY SOURCE

Lucy: The Beginnings of Humankind

Possible responses:

1. at Locality 162, a gully at Hadar, which is located in the desert about 100 miles northeast of Addis Ababa, Ethiopia

2. because no one had ever found so many parts from such an old skeleton; because it is difficult to find the kind of rare fossils they are looking for; because nothing like it had ever been discovered before

3. when the earliest humans lived, what early people looked like, how tall people were, how long they lived

Chapter 1, Section 2
PRIMARY SOURCE

Lascaux Cave Painting

1. Similarities may include consistent use of images, styles, and pigments. Differences may include types of painting surfaces, varying levels of complexity, and states of preservation. When students assemble their display, encourage them to group paintings by location and to label where the cave paintings are found.

2. Students may find that prehistoric artists created cave paintings by drawing with brushes made of green twigs or by blowing pigment from a reed or hollow bone. They used paints made from charcoal, animal blood, ocher, clay, and other materials. To help students understand the process of making cave paintings, you may want to invite an art teacher from your school to speak to the class.

3. Students' research should reveal such strategies as limiting public access, providing guards, and using surveillance cameras to protect sites where cave paintings are located. Encourage students to devise their own lists of suggestions for preserving cave art.

Chapter 1, Section 2
PRIMARY SOURCE

"Window on the Stone Age"

1. Informally assess students' diary entries to make sure they have incorporated details from the article. As an alternative, you may want to have pairs of students role-play an interview with Chauvet.

2. Informally assess students' participation in the debate. Remind them to support their arguments for or against unlimited public access with facts and reasons.

Chapter 1, Section 1
LITERATURE SELECTION

The Clan of the Cave Bear

1. Students should draw on specific details in this passage related to the average height and build of men and women. In particular, they should mention such details as large bones; bowed legs and arms; large heads; large, beaky noses; jutting jaws; no chin; low, sloping foreheads; short, thick necks; and an abundance of body hair. Both men and women walk barefoot and wear leather hides; men also wear outer fur wraps.

Possible responses:

2. Men hunt game with clubs, wooden spears, and slingshots. Using pointed digging sticks and their hands, women gather berries, fruits, newts, grubs, molluscs, and edible plants such as day lilies, cattails, clover, alfalfa, dandelion, and thistles.

3. because she does not belong to the clan; because she is badly injured and will likely die; because they are preoccupied with hunting food and finding a new cave to live in; because she is different and they fear her

4. Unlike present-day Americans, Auel's characters belong to a clan headed by a man, live in caves, hunt and gather food, dress in animal hides, and lack written language. In addition, they are nomadic, have relatively short lifespans, and lack a complex spoken language. On the other hand, clan members do hold religious beliefs, perform rituals, and use tools.

Chapter 1, Section 1
HISTORYMAKERS

Mary Leakey

Possible responses:

1. Louis Leakey was a good promoter and raised funds for their work, but Mary was excellent at finding fossils and recording and preserving them for scientific study.

2. Mary Leakey found the prehuman named *Proconsul*, an ancient creature whose skull she reconstructed from 400 pieces, a sample of *Homo habilis*, and examples of ancient footprints that showed early hominids had walked upright.

3. Leakey seemed to enjoy digging into the earth and finding evidence of human and prehuman life.

Chapter 1, Section 2
HISTORYMAKERS

The Iceman

Possible responses:

1. The body of the Iceman was revealed when hot sand blew from Africa and melted snow in the European Alps.

2. The Iceman placed grass inside his shoes, wore a cape made of grass, and used animal skins for a shirt and pants.

3. The Iceman probably ate game hunted by bow and arrow, possibly cooked on a fire, and ate wheat or other grains.

Chapter 1, Section 3
CONNECTIONS ACROSS TIME AND CULTURES

Possible responses:

1. Many of today's jobs are in government, manufacturing and retail, technology, science and medicine, and service industries.

2. The layout would be more complex and extensive because of zoning laws and vast communication and transportation networks. Housing today is generally more spacious than in Ur. Businesses might include large manufacturing plants and retailing of a wide variety of goods and services.

3. In both a bazaar and mall, people buy and sell goods and services.

4. Answers may include some of the characteristics noted below.

   Advanced cities: Ur—center for trade; Your community—part of trade network; products from distant places

   Specialized workers: Ur—farmers, irrigation workers, artisans, merchants, priests; Your community—many specialists in manufacturing, communications, retail services

   Record keeping: Ur—cuneiform records of business, public events; Your community—computer data of sales, payments, and so forth; public records of births, marriages, laws, lawsuits, and other matters

   Complex institutions: Ur—government, religion, education; Your community—governments, religions, education, charities, corporations

   Advanced technology: Ur—irrigation, bronze work, pottery; Your community—telecommunications, automobiles, space exploration

Chapter 1, Section 1
RETEACHING

1. A culture is a people's unique way of life.

2. diet, clothing, sports, tools and technology, customs, work

3. family, class and caste structure, government, economic system, view of authority, relationships between individual and community

4. media, family, friends, government, religious institutions, school, workplace

5. f

6. b

7. e

8. a

9. c

10. d

Chapter 1, Section 2
RETEACHING

1. c

2. d

3. c

4. b

5. a

6. b

7. a / d

8. c

Chapter 1, Section 3
RETEACHING

1. A city is a center of trade for a large area, providing markets for local farmers, merchants, and traders, as well as goods city dwellers produced themselves for exchange.

2. Ur in Sumer

3. The need for specialized workers grew as cities grew. People began to become experts in a particular type of work.

4. government official, priest, potter, metalworker, or other artisan

5. Growing cities required a system of government and established laws.

6. government, religion, economy

7. As institutions became more complex, people needed to be able to keep track of taxes, grain storage, and the passage of time.

8. cuneiform, pictographs

9. New tools and equipment were needed to make life easier for growing groups of people. This occurred both in farming and in the work of artisans.

10. ox-drawn plows, irrigation systems, potter's wheel, invention of bronze

11. f

12. b

13. d

14. c

15. e

16. a

Chapter 2, Section 1
GUIDED READING

A. Possible responses:

1. construct irrigation systems to carry river water to fields

2. build city walls with mud bricks

3. trade grain, cloth, and tools for products they lacked

4. give military leaders permanent control of standing armies and in turn city-states; set up dynasties

5. build ziggurats and offer sacrificed animals, food, and wine to the gods

B. Possible responses:

Religion: Polytheism, believed different gods controlled forces of nature

Literature: *The Epic of Gilgamesh*

Architecture: Ziggurats, arches, columns, ramps

Inventions: wheel, sail, plow, cuneiform tablets, number system in base 60

C. Possible response: An empire is characterized by the unification of several peoples, nations, or formerly independent states under one ruler. The Babylonian ruler Hammurabi unified diverse groups within his empire by creating a uniform code of laws. Through trade and war, people come into contact with other people and exchange ideas, beliefs, and technology through the process of cultural diffusion.

Chapter 2, Section 2
GUIDED READING

A. Possible responses:

1. Menes united Upper and Lower Egypt.

2. Egyptian pharaohs were gods who ruled over government, religion, and the military. Mesopotamian kings were representatives of gods, but they themselves were not considered gods.

3. Egyptians believed kings had eternal spirits and built pyramids as resting

places from which their rulers could reign forever after death.

4. Both were polytheistic; Egyptians believed in an afterlife while Mesopotamians had a bleak view of death.

5. royal family; upper, middle, and lower classes; and slaves

6. developed a number system, form of geometry, columns in architecture, calendar, medical procedures, mummification

7. Both systems began with pictures to represent ideas.

B. Possible response: The Nile provided Egyptians with water from distant mountains, rich fertile soil, especially in the delta region, and abundant harvests. The Nile was a reliable source of transportation between Upper and Lower Egypt, two distinct regions that developed between the First Cataract, or rapids, and the Mediterranean.

Chapter 2, Section 3
GUIDED READING

A. Possible responses:

Geography: Hindu Kush, Karakoram, Himalaya ranges, and Indus-Ganges plain in north; desert in west; Deccan plateau in south; seasonal winds called monsoons

Settlements/Buildings: Planned cities with fortified citadel and uniform housing; brick buildings with plumbing and sewer systems

Religious beliefs: Worshiped major Indian god Shiva, mother goddess, fertility images, and cattle

Economic life: Farming, long-distance trade, production of nonessential goods; prosperous economy

B. Possible response: From October to May winter monsoons from the northeast blow dry air across land; spring monsoons blow from the southwest carrying great rain clouds. People of the Indus must cope with the cycle of wet and dry seasons brought by the monsoons and the severe drought and flooding that may result.

Chapter 2, Section 4
GUIDED READING

A. Possible responses:

1. Huang He and Yangtze river systems, Plateau of Tibet, Gobi Desert, Mongolian Plateau, Himalaya Mountains

2. flooding of Huang He, geographic isolation

3. walled cities; elaborate palaces, tombs, timber-framed homes within city

4. warrior-nobles and peasants

5. central authority in Chinese society; elderly had special privileges; women treated as inferiors

6. worshipped spirits of family ancestors, supreme god, and lesser gods; consulted gods through oracle bones

7. many written characters, each representing an idea

8. manufactured weapons and religious items, bronzework

9. embroidered silk clothing

B. Possible response: Zhou leaders viewed royal authority as divine, a Mandate of Heaven. To govern a vast empire, Zhou leaders established feudalism, a political system in which nobles were given control over royal lands in return for service to the king.

Chapter 2
BUILDING VOCABULARY

A. Matching

1. g
2. c
3. e
4. h
5. a
6. d
7. b
8. f

B. Multiple Choice

1. b
2. a
3. b
4. c
5. a
6. c

C. Writing

Possible Answer

The Sumerian civilization in Mesopotamia consisted of a number of city-states, each of which had its own government and own rulers. The governments of the Sumerian city-states were controlled by priests and military leaders. Some military rulers became full-time rulers and passed their power on to their sons, forming dynasties. Ancient Egypt was also controlled by dynasties, but the rulers were considered almost like gods and were called pharaohs. Archaeologists think that the Harappan civilization had a theocracy, in which rulers are believed to get their authority from the gods. The ancient Chinese were ruled by dynasties in which the king was believed to have divine approval. The Zhou dynasty established feudalism in China, a sytem in which nobles were granted the use of land that belonged to the king in exchange for loyalty and military service.

Chapter 2, Section 2
SKILLBUILDER PRACTICE

Possible responses:

1. architects, masons, stone carvers, painters; a person to design the site and the building; a person to acquire materials for the construction, a person to arrange transportation of the materials, a person to manage and direct work gangs

2. images of gods or pharaohs, events in the lives of the gods or the pharaohs, information praising the gods or the pharaohs

3. glass and ceramic jars and dishes probably holding kohl or oils

4. The design shows flowers probably found in the region; may have represented beauty or freshness.

5. Games could include: chess, checkers, cribbage; dice or a spinner.

Chapter 2, Section 2
GEOGRAPHY APPLICATION

Responses may vary on the inferential questions. Sample responses are given for those.

1. the Mediterranean Sea

2. north

3. south

4. with tiny dots

5. the Mediterranean Sea and deserts

6. more than 150 miles long; about 100 miles

7. The Nile Delta provides Egypt with more than one-half of the country's land for growing food, flowers, cotton, and other crops. It also provides water for use by about 15 million Egyptians.

8. The Nile Delta has lost any remnant of its ancient sites because back then durable building materials were not used. Drainage problems and pollution are reducing the area's fertility. The rising level of the Mediterranean Sea may flood the area in the future.

Chapter 2, Section 1
PRIMARY SOURCE

Assyrian Letters

Possible responses:

1. They haven't received the silver that is owed to them and they have tried to contact the debtors to no avail for 30 years.

2. They will hear from their local ruler and authorities and will lose their standing as respected merchants in the community.

3. She has not provided him with clothes that suit his social standing.

4. The first letter reveals the merchants' honorable attitude and patience toward the debtors, while the second letter reveals Iddin-Sin's selfish, petty, and disrespectful attitude toward his mother.

5. Students may draw any of these conclusions: Mesopotamians had some of the same concerns and problems that people do today; communication was difficult; merchants were esteemed members of the community; local rulers and authorities worked together to uphold ethical conduct; parent-child relationships were similar to the way parents and children relate today.

Chapter 2, Section 1
PRIMARY SOURCE

The Code of Hammurabi

1. Informally assess students' role-playing to make sure they understand the laws and the penalties for breaking the laws.

2. Before students begin this activity, have them draw up a list of questions to ask the guest speaker. Help them understand the major differences between Hammurabi's Code and our legal system today. The code was an informal collection of select legal decisions on specific situations. However, the United States has a formal legal system with broader recommended rules of justice. Hammurabi's Code is stricter than U.S. law, frequently recommending death or a "punishment that fits the crime"—a penalty that reflects almost exactly the nature of the crime. The work of doctors seems unappreciated, for they are punished for failed operations in Hammurabi's Code. The code is inconsistent to women; in a particular situation, a woman will have some rights but not others.

Chapter 2, Section 2
PRIMARY SOURCE

Sphinx of Amenemhet III

1. Features might include hieroglyphics, the use of black granite, the use of details to create a lifelike portrait of the pharaoh and a realistic lion's body, the pharaoh's stern expression, association of the pharaoh with a lion's strength and power, the depiction of mythological sphinx, the damage that occurred over time.

2. Possible responses: the importance of pharaohs in Egyptian society, traits Egyptians admired, native materials used to create sculpture, Egyptians' artistry and skill in carving stone, existence of a writing system, and Egyptians' keen observation of nature

3. Comparisons will vary but should include similarities and differences in such aspects as size, subject, medium, materials, and the use of realistic or abstract forms.

Chapter 2, Section 1
LITERATURE SELECTION

Ancient Proverbs

1. Choices will vary. Students should offer reasonable explanations for their selections.

2. Possible response: The importance of behaving ethically and responsibly is expressed.

3. Some students may say that the proverbs reflect Mesopotamians' concern with moderation, prudent behavior, integrity, and compassion. Others may say that the proverbs reveal cynicism and intolerance.

Chapter 2, Section 1
LITERATURE SELECTION

The Epic of Gilgamesh

Possible responses:

1. Similarities: a great flood covers the earth, all people and animals not on the hero's boat are drowned, the hero is spared. Differences: the Biblical story involves Noah instead of Pernapishtim; God causes it to rain rather than Adad, Ninib, and other gods; it rains for 40 days instead of 6; Noah's boat stops at Ararat instead of Mount Nisir; Noah first sends a raven and then a dove to see if flood waters have receded instead of dove, swallow, and raven.

2. Through their research, students will find that an epic is a long narrative poem on a serious subject presented in an elevated or formal style. An epic typically traces the adventures of a hero whose actions consist of courageous, even superhuman deeds, which often represent a culture's ideals and values. They may list such epics as the Greek *Iliad* and the *Odyssey*, the Anglo-Saxon poem *Beowulf*, the Indian Mahabharata, and the German *Nibelungenlied*.

Chapter 2, Section 1
HISTORYMAKERS

Hammurabi

Possible responses:

1. Hammurabi's two achievements were to unite much of Mesopotamia under the rule of Babylon and to write his code of laws.

2. Hammurabi was probably concerned about his image. The stele with the code shows him receiving the laws from a god, and the writing at first describes his many conquests.

3. Students may see Hammurabi as a just king. He hoped that his code would "prevent the powerful from oppressing the weak [and] . . . give [his] land fair decisions." Others may feel that the harsh penalties, the varying treatment of different classes, and the power of

fathers over their families were unjust laws.

Chapter 2, Section 2
HISTORYMAKERS

Tutankhamen

Possible responses:

1. Akhenaten's rule caused trouble in Egypt because he neglected the people and created turmoil by changing the religion.

2. In changing his name, Tutankhamen showed that he supported the old gods and not the new god of his father, which had caused such difficulty.

3. Archaeologists can learn much about everyday life by studying shoes, boxes, food, and other artifacts.

Chapter 2, Section 4
CONNECTIONS ACROSS TIME AND CULTURES

Possible responses:

1. Other problems included watering fields during dry months and destruction of villages by the flooding.

2. Irrigation systems were built to carry river water to fields. Governments emerged and laws were passed to settle disputes over land and water distribution.

3. Poorly maintained irrigation canals reduced the amount of water available for crops. Without water, the land could not produce crops. If they did not keep the canals open, people would have to move or starve. An invading army might kill many inhabitants, but life could continue if farmers had water for their crops.

4. There may not have been enough available manpower to maintain the canals; maybe canal workers were in too much danger from enemy attack. In addition, invaders may have deliberately tried to cut off water supplies from cities they attacked.

5. People of the Indus Valley had to cope with a cycle of wet and dry seasons brought by the monsoon winds. Egypt and Mesopotamia received little rainfall. In the Indus Valley, too little rain withered the crops; too much rain brought destructive floods.

6. It takes organization, cooperation, leadership, and advance planning to create solutions to environmental problems. New ideas often arise from practical needs.

Chapter 2, Section 3
SCIENCE & TECHNOLOGY

Possible responses:

1. First, Sumerian farmers carried water to their fields. Then they cut holes in the river banks to drain water to the farmland. They also built reservoirs, dug canals, and would break a hole in a canal to flood a tract of land.

2. A shaduf is a bucket attached to a counter-weighted pole. It was used to lift water from the reservoirs to the fields.

3. It is both easier to water and there is more water available to a field when there is a canal or waterway next to it

Chapter 2, Section 1
RETEACHING

1. Fertile Crescent
2. Mesopotamia
3. Tigris, Euphrates
4. drought, flooding
5. Sumer
6. civilization
7. dynasty
8. cultural diffusion
9. polytheism
10. empire
11. cuneiform
12. Hammurabi

Chapter 2, Section 2
RETEACHING

1. provided yearly water that allowed farming settlements to grow; Egyptians worshiped the river as a god because of its abundance.

2. Low waters in the Nile resulted in famine because of poor crops; flooding sometimes destroyed houses and crops.

3. shut out invaders and spared Egypt constant warfare

4. acted as barriers between Egypt and other lands; forced Egyptians to live on a very small portion of the land; reduced interactions with other peoples

5. pharoahs
6. theocracy
7. pyramid
8. mummification
9. hieroglyphics
10. papyrus

Chapter 2, Section 3
RETEACHING

1. Indian subcontinent
2. Hindu Kush, Karakoram, and Himalayan mountain ranges
3. monsoons
4. unpredictable flooding, changes in course of rivers, too much rain or too little rain for crops
5. Harappan civilization; because of the large number of archaeological discoveries made in Harappa
6. use of a precise grid system for streets, major city buildings concentrated in the citadel, bricks cut in standard sizes, complex plumbing and sewage systems
7. because no artifact has been found that is written in a recognizable language along with the Indus Valley language
8. social divisions in the society were not emphasized; few weapons found, so conflict was probably limited; animals were an important part of the culture; prosperous society that could afford to produce nonessential goods; close ties to religion
9. gold, silver, semiprecious stones, cotton cloth
10. earthquakes and floods

Chapter 2, Section 4
RETEACHING

1. H, K
2. N
3. A
4. D
5. J
6. B

7. G

8. C

9. L

10. F

11. I

12. M

Chapter 3, Section 1
GUIDED READING

A. Possible responses:

1. steppes

2. Anatolia

3. Babylon

4. chariots

5. iron

6. Aryans

7. castes

8. brahmins

9. untouchables or shudras

10. Magadha

11. and 12. Spanish, German, English, Persian, Sanskrit

B. Possible responses:

The *Vedas,* four collections of prayers, magical spells, and rituals, are sacred Indian literature and a reliable source of information about Aryan life.

Mahabharata is an Indian epic that describes a struggle between two sets of cousins that took place as the Aryans moved south.

Chapter 3, Section 2
GUIDED READING

A. Possible responses:

1. Hinduism: Collection of religious beliefs that developed over time; no founder

   Buddhism: Siddhartha Gautama

2. Hinduism: Interconnectedness of all life; distinction between atman, soul of individuals, and Brahman, world soul; reincarnation of soul or spirit; good and bad karma; ultimate goal of moksha, state of perfect understanding

   Buddhism: Four Noble Truths; an Eightfold Path to attain enlightenment;

reincarnation, ultimate goal of nirvana, release from selfishness and pain

3. Hinduism: Many gods including Brahma, the creator; Vishnu, the protector; Shiva, the destroyer; later, many forms of a great Mother Goddess

   Buddhism: Enlightenment in place of many gods

4. Hinduism: *Upanishads, Vedas*

   Buddhism: Written teachings of Buddha, commentaries, rules about monastic life, how-to-meditate manuals, and Buddha legends

5. Hinduism: Ideas of karma and reincarnation strengthened caste system. Hindu religion dominates daily activities.

   Buddhism: Rejected caste system; created religious communities of monks and nuns within society

6. Hinduism: Freedom to choose among three paths for achieving moksha and the deity to worship

   Buddhism: Daily declaration of "Three Jewels of Buddhism," pilgrimages to sites associated with Buddha's life, performing of Buddhist worship rituals

B. Possible response: Followers of Jainism believe everything in the universe has a soul and should not be harmed. They practice tolerance and nonviolence and work in occupations in which they do not harm other creatures.

Chapter 3, Section 3
GUIDED READING

A. Possible responses:

1. Minoans were a peaceful, not warlike, people, or they lived during a time of peace.

2. Minoans had some form of government and a culture that created and appreciated fine arts.

3. Women held a high rank in Minoan society; Minoans practiced organized religion.

4. The bull had special significance in Minoan history and culture.

5. The Phoenicians were skilled shipbuilders and sailors.

6. The Phoenicians were resourceful and skilled artisans.

7. Phoenician traders spread their alphabet system to the peoples with whom they traded.

B. Possible response: Archaeologists who excavated Knossos, the Minoan capital built on Crete, a large island in the Aegean Sea, named the ancient people who had lived there "Minoans" after legendary King Minos.

Chapter 3, Section 4
GUIDED READING

A. Possible responses:

1. the Torah

2. At first the Hebrews held places of honor in the Egyptian kingdom, but later they were forced into slavery.

3. Moses led the Hebrews out of slavery and received the Ten Commandments from God.

4. Saul drove the Philistines out of central Palestine; David united the tribes, made Jerusalem the capital, and began a dynasty.

5. to glorify God and house the Ark of the Covenant

6. High taxes and forced labor caused discontent resulting in the revolt of Jews living in the northern part of the kingdom.

7. Chaldean king who twice attacked Jerusalem

8. Persian king Cyrus

B. Possible response: The area of Palestine called Canaan was home to the Hebrews, who practiced monotheism. They believed in one God, Yahweh, who had made a covenant with Abraham to protect his descendants if they promised to obey him.

Chapter 3
BUILDING VOCABULARY

A. Matching

1. d

2. f

3. a

4. b

5. g

6. h

7. e

8. c

B. Evaluating

1. T

2. F In a caste system, people are born into their caste and remain in it for life.

3. F Knossos was a Minoan capital city that was the center of an advanced and peaceful culture.

4. T

5. F The Hebrews were united under kings Saul, David, and Solomon in a kingdom called Israel.

C. Writing

Possible Answer

In Hinduism, the goal is to achieve moksha, a state of perfect understanding. A person arrives at moksha by understanding the relationship between an individual's soul and the world soul that contains and unites all souls. Until moksha is achieved, an individual soul is born again and again in a process called <u>reincarnation.</u> A soul's good or bad deeds, called <u>karma,</u> follow from one reincarnation to another. A person who reaches moksha is released from life in this world. Like Hinduism, Buddhism includes the idea of reincarnation and a search for <u>enlightenment,</u> or wisdom. The goal of Buddhism is <u>nirvana,</u> a release from selfishness and pain. Nirvana is similar to moksha. Distinctive features of Judaism include an emphasis on right conduct and the worship of one god, which is called <u>monotheism.</u>

Chapter 3, Section 3
SKILLBUILDER PRACTICE

Possible responses:

Opinion: Minoan civilization was highly advanced and enlightened for its time.

Supporting Details:

Indoor plumbing

Complex buildings, towns connected by roads

Appreciation of fine arts and the theater

Equal treatment of women

Long-distance trade

Chapter 3, Section 4
GEOGRAPHY APPLICATION

Responses may vary on the inferential questions. Sample responses are given for those.

1. Hittites, Minoans, Phoenicians, Hebrews, and Philistines

2. the Hittites; At one time, they controlled a stretch of Mediterranean area land from the Aegean Sea east to Babylon.

3. Byblos, Sidon, Tyre, and Jerusalem

4. They were an island civilization in the middle of the Mediterranean Sea.

5 the Phoenicians; They had three major seaports on the Mediterranean.

6 the Phoenicians and the Philistines

Chapter 3, Section 1
PRIMARY SOURCE

Rig Veda

1. Informally assess students' recitation and their participation in the discussion.

2. Encourage students to display their sketches or to create illustrated posters using their sketch and the text of the hymn.

Chapter 3, Section 1
PRIMARY SOURCE

Bhagavad-Gita

Possible responses:

1. dejected, fearful, discouraged, grief-stricken

2. because he believes the destruction of a family is a sin; because he feels that the ruin of a family causes chaos and disorder in society

3. the importance of family relationships, family duty, order in society, and the caste system

Chapter 3, Section 3
PRIMARY SOURCE

Dolphin Fresco from Knossos

1. Through research, students will learn that *fresco* derives from the Italian word meaning "fresh." Frescoes are paintings that are painted on fresh, moist plaster with pigments dissolved in water. Italian painters Giotto and

Michelangelo are known for their frescoes.

2. Students' reports will vary but may include observations as follows: styles of dress, customs, social structure, religious beliefs and rituals, forms of entertainment, love of nature, and importance of the sea.

3. Charts will vary but should include some of the following facts: The palace, which covered about 20,000 square meters and housed about 5,000 people, served as the royal residence as well as an administrative, religious, economic, and food storage and redistribution center. British archaeologist Sir Arthur Evans excavated the ruins.

Chapter 3, Section 4
PRIMARY SOURCE

The Ten Commandments

Possible responses:

1 by worshiping one god, by not making or worshiping carved idols or fetishes, by not taking the Lord's name in vain; by observing the Sabbath as a day of rest

2. by honoring their parents, by not committing murder or adultery, by not stealing, by not bearing false witness against their neighbors, by not desiring what their neighbors have

3. The Ten Commandments teach a belief in one god instead of many.

Chapter 3, Section 2
LITERATURE SELECTION

Ramayana

1. Informally assess students' comic strips to make certain that they accurately reflect the text of this excerpt. You may want to suggest that they work together to compile a comic book.

2. Before students begin, provide them with models of front-page news stories. Then informally assess students' newspaper reports, and have them share their work with the class.

3. Before they begin this activity, tell students that they may either compose original music or set their lyrics to an existing piece of music. Then informally assess students' songs. Encourage them to perform their songs for the class.

Chapter 3, Section 2
LITERATURE SELECTION

Siddhartha

Possible responses:

1. dissatisfied, discontented, afraid of himself

2. At first he feels exhilarated, eager to learn about himself, and full of purpose; as he contemplates the meaning of his awakening, he feels alone and overwhelmed.

3. Students may indicate any of the following: he is serious, thoughtful, reflective, contemplative, courageous, spiritual, isolated, lonely, disciplined, open-minded.

Chapter 3, Section 2
HISTORYMAKERS

Siddhartha Gautama

Possible responses:

1. In the quotation at the top of the page, the Buddha urges people to try to use good—love, being generous, and telling the truth—to change the behavior of people doing evil.

2. Most students will suggest that much in life is good—whether it is beneficial to other people or enjoyable for oneself. They may not agree that all life is suffering.

3. The Buddha did not support the Hindu caste system, which could undermine Hindu society.

Chapter 3, Section 3
HISTORYMAKERS

Herodotus

Possible responses:

1. Herodotus may have called his work "inquiries" to underscore that he was trying to answer questions about what had happened before.

2. As a Greek—a citizen of the nation that the Persians had attacked—Herodotus is unlikely to be objective about the Persians. He probably was negative toward them.

3. A work is a history when it tries as truthfully as possible to tell the story of what happened in the past. It must be done in an organized way and attempt to explain why things occurred.

Chapter 3, Section 4
CONNECTIONS ACROSS TIME AND CULTURES

Possible responses:

1. Their beliefs are similar to those of Hinduism, which is also polytheistic. They are different from the beliefs of Buddhism, which rejects the worship of any gods at all, emphasizing enlightenment instead. They are also different from those of Judaism, which believed in one god.

2. The ancient Hebrews maintained their religion while traveling because they believed God did not belong in one place. They could worship him anywhere.

3. The ancient Hebrews worshiped God for years before they began to be ruled by a king. The king was a political leader, but he had the same duty to worship God as any other Hebrew.

4. Although the ancient Hebrews made sacrifices to God, they emphasized a promise to obey God.

5. Both Hinduism and Buddhism believed that humans would be reborn after death to live again in the world of suffering. When a soul finally attained perfect understanding, or enlightenment, it was released from the cycle of rebirth into a peaceful state.

Chapter 3, Section 1
RETEACHING

1. a. The region they came from was known as the steppes, stretches of dry grasslands.

   b. The Indo-Europeans were a pastoral people who herded cattle, sheep, and goats and tamed horses.

2. a. English, Spanish, Persian, and Hindi all originated from the original Indo-European languages.

   b. Slavic-speakers moved north and west, while Aryans, who spoke an early form of Sanskrit, entered India.

3. a. The Hittites occupied Anatolia, also called Asia Minor, a peninsula that juts out into the Black and Mediterranean seas.

   b. The city of Hattusas was the capital of the Hittite empire.

4. a. They had superior war chariots that were light, easy to maneuver, and pulled by horses.

   b. The Hittites were the first in Southwest Asia to harden iron into weapons of war.

5. a. Their homeland was believed to be somewhere between the Caspian and Aral seas.

   b. The sacred literature of the Aryans were the Vedas, four collections of prayers, magical spells, and instructions for rituals. The most important was the *Rig Veda*.

6. a. The Aryans were taller, lighter in skin color, and spoke a different language.

   b. The Aryans were a pastoral people, unlike the *dasas,* who were town dwellers.

7. a. The classes were Brahmans or priests, warriors, and peasants or traders.

   b. A person's class determined his or her role in society.

8. a. There were four basic castes: Brahmans (priests), Kshatriyas (rulers and warriors), Vaishyas (peasants and traders), and Shudras (laborers).

   b. People were born into their caste for life, which determined the work they did, the person they could marry, and the people with whom they could eat.

Chapter 3, Section 2
RETEACHING

1. Hinduism cannot be traced back to one founder with a single set of ideas. It is a collection of religious beliefs that developed over centuries.

2. Buddhism was founded by Siddhartha Gautama, who became known as the Buddha.

3. three main gods: Brahma, Vishnu, and Shiva

4. Buddhists do not worship a god.

5. guru, Brahmin priest

6. Buddhist monks and nuns

7. the Vedas, the Puranas

8. the *Verses of Righteousness*

9. belief in reincarnation, the rebirth of an individual soul or spirit until a perfect state is achieved

10. belief that karma, a person's good or bad deeds, follows the person from one reincarnation to another

11. follow the path of right thinking, right action, and religious devotion

12. followers seek a state of enlightenment, or wisdom

13. belief in the Four Noble Truths: 1) life is filled with suffering and sorrow; 2) The cause of all suffering is selfish desire for temporary pleasures; 3) The way to end all suffering is to end all desires; 4) the way to overcome desires is to follow the Eightfold Path.

14. The Eightfold Path, or Middle Way, includes Right Views, Right Resolve, Right Speech, Right Conduct, Right Livelihood, Right Effort, Right Mindfulness, and Right Concentration.

15. strengthened the caste system

16. rejected the caste system

Chapter 3, Section 3
RETEACHING

1. b
2. a
3. d
4. d
5. a
6. b
7. d
8. c

Chapter 3, Section 4
RETEACHING

1. part of Palestine that was the ancient home of the Hebrews; According to the Bible, Canaan was the land God had promised to the Hebrew people.

2. later became known as the Jews

3. the first five books of the Hebrew Bible, considered the most sacred writings in their tradition

4. led the Hebrews out of slavery in Egypt; received the Ten Commandments from God on Mount Sinai

5. code of laws delivered to Moses; serve as the basis for Jewish law

6. Abraham

7. monotheism

8. Yahweh

9. Philistines

10. Israel

11. tribute

12. Judaism

Chapter 4, Section 1
GUIDED READING

A. Possible responses:

1. around 1600 B.C.; helped drive Hyksos out of Egypt

2. around 1472 B.C.; encouraged trade

3. after death of Hatshepsut to around 1425 B.C.; built a mighty empire through victorious invasions into Palestine, Syria, and Nubia

4. about 1290 B.C.–1224 B.C.; made a treaty with Hittites that brought peace for rest of century; built great monuments including temple at Abu Simbel

5. 950 B.C.–730 B.C.; erected cities, established independent dynasties

6. 751 B.C.–671 B.C.; overthrew Libyan dynasty, united Nile Valley, established Twenty-fifth Dynasty

B. Possible response: For centuries after Thutmose III added Nubia, a region south of Egypt, to the Egyptian Empire, the history and culture of these regions intertwined. Kush, a great kingdom in Nubia, viewed itself as the guardian of Egyptian values and conquered Egypt by overthrowing the Libyan dynasty.

C. Possible response: Unlike the warlike New Kingdom, Meroë became a prosperous center of trade. Like the pharaohs, Kushite kings were great builders. However, they did not establish dynasties.

Chapter 4, Section 2
GUIDED READING

A. Possible responses:

Weapons and equipment: Iron-tipped spears and battering rams, daggers, and swords; armor and helmets, leather skirt with metal scales

Military tactics: Advance planning, which involved building bridges and weakening city walls; assaulting besieged city with arrows; ramming open gates and storming city

Method of governing: Organized conquered territories into a system of dependent provinces ruled by Assyrian officials or kings aligned with Assyria; used military power and cruelty to control empire.

Culture: Built magnificent cities and buildings, created fine carved sculptures, valued reading and writing

B. Possible response: Assyrians overextended themselves and made many enemies, two of which, the Medes and Chaldeans, combined their armies and destroyed Nineveh, the Assyrian capital.

Chapter 4, Section 3
GUIDED READING

A. Possible responses:

King Cyrus:
Founded Persian Empire
Allowed conquered people freedom
Allowed Jews to return to Jerusalem
Governed wisely and tolerantly

King Darius:
Spent early years putting down revolts
Established organized, efficient government
Built system of roads
Introduced standardized money and promoted trade
Ruled with absolute power

Both:
Military genius
Practiced tolerance
Honored customs and religions of "nationalities"

B. Possible response: Darius exercised absolute control over his empire by installing satraps to rule locally and then sending inspectors to check on each satrap's loyalty. He built the Royal Road to aid the spread of commerce and ideas throughout the empire.

C. Possible response: Each person takes part in the struggle between the spirit of good and the spirit of evil. Ahura Mazda, the Zoroastrian god, will judge everyone according to how well he or she fought.

Chapter 4, Section 4
GUIDED READING

A. Possible responses:

1. Confucius; social order should be based on basic relationships among people; education and a trained civil service essential for good government

2. Laozi; understanding nature is key to order and harmony; universal force called Dao guides all things

3. Hanfeizi, Li Si; efficient and powerful government is key to order; government should control ideas and use law and punishment to restore harmony

B. Possible response: Two opposite but complementary powers represent the rhythm of the universe. This concept of balanced opposites helped people understand their place in the world.

C. Possible response: Shi Huangdi, a Qin dynasty ruler, established an autocracy in which he used cruel measures and built the Great Wall to crush political opposition and unify his empire.

Chapter 4
BUILDING VOCABULARY

A. Matching

1. e
2. h
3. a
4. d
5. g
6. b
7. f
8. c

B. Completion

1. New Kingdom
2. Royal Road
3. Zoroaster
4. Nineveh
5. bureaucracy
6. autocracy

C. Writing

Possible Answer

In the chaotic period near the end of the Zhou dynasty, Chinese philosophers sought to restore ancient values of social order, harmony, and respect for authority. Confucius developed a code of conduct that stressed respect, loyalty, kindness, courtesy, and virtuous living. Laozi developed the philosophy known as Daoism, which taught that people should follow the natural order. A group of practical political thinkers promoted Legalism, which was based on the belief that government should use the law and rewards and punishments to end civil disorder. Some Chinese found answers to their questions and problems in the *I Ching*, a book of oracles that offered advice based on common sense. Others turned to ancient ideas, such as the concept of yin and yang, two complementary powers that represent life's natural rhythms.

Chapter 4, Section 4
SKILLBUILDER PRACTICE

Possible responses:

2. Effect/Cause: Nobles begin using their armies to fight each other over land.

4. Effect: Without loyalty and protection of nobles, Zhou Dynasty weakens.

6. Effect/Cause: Surviving feudal states become powerful. Chaos and social disorder replace traditional Chinese values.

8. Effect: A power struggle follows and the ruler of Qin seizes control of China.

Chapter 4, Section 2
GEOGRAPHY APPLICATION

Responses may vary on the inferential questions. Sample responses are given for those.

1. It is about 2,500 yards long.

2. Processional Way

3. the New City

4. They could cross the Euphrates more easily. In addition, they could also wheel carts and other things across it. Boats, however, would be easier to remove in case of attack.

5. There is a moat, canals, and the Euphrates River. The moat is used for protection, the canals are used for transportation and communication, and the river is used for irrigation, traveling, and transporting. However, the river could overflow and flood the city.

6. There is a moat, an inner and outer wall, a gate, and towers. The moat would make attacking the walls more difficult. The walls and gate would repel invaders, and towers could be used to observe approaching enemies and forewarn invasion.

Chapter 4, Section 2
PRIMARY SOURCE

Assyrian Capture of Jerusalem

1. Informally assess students' headlines to make sure they reflect both the historical content of the selection and an appropriate point of view.

2. Informally assess students' role-playing to make sure they draw on details in this selection.

Chapter 4, Section 3
PRIMARY SOURCE

"To the Fire"

Possible responses:

1. salvation, prosperity, understanding

2. wood, perfume, sacred butter, andirons

3. Students will likely say a god of truth and light because Fire is the son of Ahura Mazda, the god of truth and light in the Zoroastrian religion.

Chapter 4, Section 4
PRIMARY SOURCE

Intrigues of the Warring States

Possible responses:

1. The king shares his power with his greedy minister Jang-hou and others, thereby weakening his authority and threatening the unity of Ch'in.

2. He compares Ch'in to a Sacred Grove that dies when it lends its power to someone else and to a gourd that one man can deliver but that would be split apart if it were carried by one hundred men. He also points out that great rulers in the past maintained control and order because they did not allow their ministers to become too strong.

3. Students will likely say that Ying-hou would tell the king to rule absolutely and to keep Jang-hou and other power-hungry members of the royal court in check.

Chapter 4, Section 4
PRIMARY SOURCE

Analects

1. Informally assess students' lists to make sure they understand what Confucius taught.

2. Informally assess students' role-playing.

Chapter 4, Section 1
LITERATURE SELECTION

Ozymandias

1. Informally assess students' photographs. You may want to have students create a bulletin board display using the photographs that they find.

2. Students will likely agree because their research will show that Ramses II was a very powerful pharaoh who is now only remembered by ruins in the desert.

Chapter 4, Section 2
LITERATURE SELECTION

The Destruction of Sennacherib

1. Students will point out that Byron adds details to the poem that do not appear in the Biblical story, such as what the Assyrians look like before the Angel of Death appears, and omits that 185,000 Assyrians were killed and Sennacherib was later murdered by his sons.

2. Galilee is a freshwater lake of northeast Israel, Ashur is Assyria, and Baal is the supreme god of the Assyrians.

Chapter 4, Section 3
LITERATURE SELECTION

Babylon

1. Informally assess students' discussions to make sure they understand the negative views of the Egyptian, Assyrian, and Babylonian empires that the poets express.

2. Before students begin, suggest that they use the poems by Shelley, Byron, and Tennyson as models. Make sure they understand that they can write about any of the first empires they have read about. Then informally assess students' poems. Encourage them to read their poems to the class.

Chapter 4, Section 1
HISTORYMAKERS

Hatshepsut

Possible responses:

1. Hatshepsut needed some allies in her grab for power. Having the backing of court officials including the top priest and the head of the treasury could help win the support of their followers.

2. Hatshepsut's reign is most remembered for the trade expedition to the south and the creation of two obelisks for the temple at Karnak.

3. Thutmose III may have tried to remove his aunt's name to discredit her reign or simply acted in anger over how she had treated him.

Chapter 4, Section 2
HISTORYMAKERS

Sennacherib

Possible responses:

1. Most students will say that the inscription saying that Sennacherib cared for Assyria is the more appropriate one because he took many good steps for his people in building Nineveh.

2. Sennacherib must have been resourceful to come up with the plan of moving the ships across land.

3. Sennacherib attacked other kingdoms that tried to challenge his power.

Chapter 4, Section 2
CONNECTIONS ACROSS TIME AND CULTURES

Possible responses:

1. iron weapons, protective armor and shields, advanced planning tactics, technical skills

2. Mesopotamia, southern Anatolia, Syria, Palestine, and Egypt

3. Grand buildings and cities, art showing military victories. Ashurbanipal, at least, valued literature.

4. about 250 years

5. alliance of Persians, Medes, and others

6. Perhaps the lesson that savage treatment of conquered peoples can lead to your own downfall; perhaps improvements in military equipment and tac-

tics; perhaps the preservation of information in the ruins of the library at Nineveh

Chapter 4, Section 1
RETEACHING

1. Hyksos
2. New Kingdom
3. Hatshepsut
4. Thutmose III
5. Nubia
6. Ramses
7. Valley of the Kings
8. dynasty
9. Piankhi
10. Assyrians
11. Meroë
12. Aksum

Chapter 4, Section 2
RETEACHING

1. B, F
2. H
3. C
4. N
5. A
6. E
7. G, K
8. J
9. M
10. D
11. O

Chapter 4, Section 3
RETEACHING

1. military genius who was king of Persia; eventually controlled an empire that covered 2,000 miles

2. son of Cyrus; expanded the Persian Empire by conquering Egypt; scorned the Egyptian religion

3. Cambyses's successor; established a well-organized and efficient administration; built a system of roads that improved communication throughout the empire

4. a governor of each of the provinces established by Darius

5. built during Darius's reign; ran from Susa in Persia to Sardix in Anatolia; promoted trade

6. Persian prophet who taught that the earth is a battleground between good and evil; taught a belief in one god, Ahura Mazda; today, followers of Zoraostrianism are called Parsis

7. Cyrus used his military genius to expand the Persian Empire until it ran from the Indus River in the east to Anatolia in the west. His legacy is his method of governing. He showed kindness to conquered peoples by preventing looting and burning and honoring local customs and religions. Cyrus allowed the Jews to return to Jerusalem.

8. Darius first brought peace and stability to the empire. Then he extended the empire through conquest to over 2,500 miles. He divided his empire into 20 provinces, but allowed each province to determine its own religion, speak its own language, and follow many of its own laws. Darius built an excellent system of roads and began the manufacturing of metal coins to make trade easier.

Chapter 4, Section 4
RETEACHING

1. Confucius

2. filial piety

3. bureaucracy

4. Daoism

5. Legalism

6. *I Ching*

7. ying and yang

8. Qin

9. Shi Huangdi

10. autocracy

11. standardizing of weights and measures, irrigation projects, expanded trade

12. Han